The AVIATION ENTHUSIAST'S Handbook

The AVIATION

ENTHUSIAST'S

Handbook

KEVIN M. FOX

ARGUS BOOKS

Argus Books
Argus House
Boundary Way
Hemel Hempstead
Herts HP2 7ST
England

First published 1991 by Argus Books
© Kevin M. Fox 1991

ISBN: 1 85486 054 2

Typeset by Photoprint, Torquay, Devon.
Printed and bound in Great Britain by
Clays Ltd, St Ives plc, Bungay.

Contents

Acknowledgements

A book which covers as much ground as this one, simply does not get written at all without a lot of help from a large number of people and companies. Response to my various requests for help was staggering, with a lot of people going to a great deal of trouble on my behalf.

I would like to thank the following for their interest in the book, their overwhelming generosity in supplying material, and their kindness to me personally.

Bob Ollerenshaw of British Airways Aerad charts service. British Airways. All the various Civil Aviation Authority departments, but particularly NATS and Publications. Scottish Air Traffic Control Centre (SCATCC) and Shanwick Oceanic at Atlantic House. The British Airports Authority, British Midland Airways.

Servisair. East Midlands, Luton, Leeds/Bradford, Manchester, Heathrow, Gatwick, Prestwick airports. Birmingham Airport – for the masses of interesting stuff, and for taking such great care of disabled spectators/travellers. The Federal Aviation Authority in the USA, for the airmailing of an incredible amount of American ATC material. Ron Moulton – whose advice was worth its weight in gold bars. Rab MacWilliam of Argus Books for all his help and patience with this, my first book.

Howes Communications. Nevada Communications. Roger Baines at South Midland Communications. The two Rogers, and Bill, all at Lowe Electronics, for putting up with me. John Wilson, also of Lowes, who let me rampage through his Airband Department at the Matlock shop, strip it clean of just about every receiver in sight, and still never batted an eyelid! Also, for saying such nice things! Thanks to Database Software – publishers of 'Stop Press' desktop publishing software – for permission to use various Clip-Art images used in the diagrams.

Finally, last but by no means least, Carlos: who drove the car, pushed the wheelchair, made the tea, constructively criticised, motivated, ranted, soothed and encouraged. The perfect friend without whose help this book could not have been written.

Introduction

This book was born of necessity, in answer to the numerous people over the years who asked me the question 'Why can't I buy just the one book which would tell me all I want to know about plane spotting?'

Well, now there is one; so welcome to my book! Within these pages you'll find some information on just about everything concerned with airports, aircraft and the fascinating world of the Plane Spotter. This is a doing kind of book, written for the newcomer. All the information and explanations within are linked to what you may see and hear directly.

I have tried to avoid detail which does not directly relate to what you may experience visually, at an airport, airfield or airshow, or listen to on an airband radio receiver. I do accept that there will be some who want additional information, and for such people there is the Bibliography, at the back of the Handbook, listing titles which cover similar material, but in much greater depth.

ABOUT THE HANDBOOK

The Handbook is in six basic parts. Part 1 deals with the complex subject of airband radio receivers, and is of necessity quite long. I make no apologies for the length. Virtually everything I've read so far on the same subject hasn't been very impressive, with information sometimes being misleading and often completely wrong. In at least one case, an author's suggested modification to an airband receiver could, and in a few cases actually did, result in that receiver's audio amplifier IC being blown to pieces! Good airband radio receivers cost a lot of money; I've tried to provide enough information for you to make an informed choice, and avoid purchasing 'a lemon'!

Part 2 deals with airport operations – the detail of how they work and make money. This part also contains a guide to British airports, providing information on how to get there, the spectator facilities available, the best viewing positions, any restrictions, charges, car parking and admission times. Also included is a list of airline companies and the airports they operate from, as well as the current Air Traffic Control radio frequencies in use.

Part 3 explains the workings of Air Traffic Control, covering airport, En-route and oceanic ATC. In this part, the information and explana-

8

tions given are linked purely to what you may see and hear directly. Any of the books in the Bibliography will provide additional background information.

Part 4 is all about the plane spotters, what they do, how they go about doing it and the equipment they use. There's lots of ideas and practical things for you to try out in this section.

Part 5 contains the Radiodatabases which give you many lists of frequencies to monitor on your airband radio receivers, and Part 6, the Appendices which contain useful addresses and brings together all those little pieces of information you often spend hours looking for in a variety of books.

BAe ATP Taxying to stand at East Midlands Airport

IMPORTANT LEGAL WARNING

Airband Radio Listening And The Law

Listening to conversations on the airbands – whether they be HF, VHF or UHF – is actually ILLEGAL. As a matter of fact, listening to anything on the radio which is not meant as a general broadcast to the public is illegal too! People have a misleading idea that it's OK to listen just as long as you don't divulge, or act upon anything you might hear. This is wrong, although I can see where this mistaken idea comes from. Only when a person is caught doing something silly is the link made to illegal listening; therefore you can *only* get into trouble if you do something silly. Although there is an element of truth to this – there must be for this rumour to have survived for so long – the basic premise is false.

This area of the Wireless Telegraphy Act is actually quite a mess, full of grey areas and to all intents and purposes, unenforceable. There is a school of thought which suggests that the onus should *not* be on stopping casual listeners from overhearing, but should be on the users, to ensure confidentiality. The Fife police in Scotland have been experimenting with a scrambling device, which ensures that their radio transmissions can only be received by authorised listeners, and indeed, this would seem to be an eminently sensible thing to do.

How To Protect Yourself

As responsible citizens we cannot choose to ignore a law of this country just because it's silly and not enforceable. Thousands of people listen every day to aeronautical radio transmissions, and the authorities are well aware of this, yet take no legal proceedings against them. As long as no one upsets the status quo – I'll explain how later – the authorities, or to be more precise, the Radiocommunications Agency, which is the government department responsible for the regulation of radio traffic in the UK, will continue this unofficial policy of 'turning a blind eye'.

You would be quite shocked to discover some of the secret information openly broadcast via radio! The unwritten rule of airband radio listening (and shortwave listening too) is: whatever you accidentally overhear, you MUST keep it to yourself. Never discuss what you've heard, or the frequency on which you heard it, at the local pub or anywhere else. This is the golden rule; as long as you keep it you will never have the slightest problem. Break it and the Radiocommunications Agency will be down on you like the proverbial ton of bricks, and so quickly it will take your breath away!

Author's Disclaimer

The Aeronautical Mobile Radio frequency information contained within this Handbook was: 1. Compiled completely from information freely available to the general public. 2. Can in no way be construed by anyone as an attempt by the author to aid and abet another person to contravene the Wireless Telegraphy Act.

All frequencies in the Radiodatabases were carefully checked and were correct at the time of writing. However, the military are notorious for changing their frequencies often; and airports do occasionally alter the frequencies of various services. Keeping an eye on the magazines which have a regular 'airband' column (lists in the Appendices) will keep you up to date with who's using what. Some of the frequencies detailed in the Radiodatabase section of the Handbook, especially the HF lists, may raise the odd eyebrow! However, as most of the information carried on these channels is either encoded or uses mechanical transmission devices, such as teleprinters or Morse keys, such data is relatively 'secure'!

HOW TO USE THE HANDBOOK

This book wasn't designed to be read from page 1 to the end, as you would a novel – although, of course, there's nothing stopping you should you prefer that. Each part is complete in itself, allowing a reader to dive in at a particular section and abstract quickly the required information. For example, there's no need to read the section on air traffic control at an airport before looking at the section on oceanic air traffic control. Naturally, as the author I would like to think that at some stage all of the Handbook will have been read!

THE PLANE SPOTTERS' CODE

Terrorist actitivies at various air terminals around the world are responsible for the current high levels of airport security. To protect yourself, and to maintain the generally high esteem with which genuine aviation enthusiasts are held, I offer the following points to bear in mind when visiting an airport.
1. Try to avoid using the passenger terminal areas.
2. Park your car only in authorised car parks.
3. Keep to the places designated as spectator areas.
4. Never leave a bag unattended, even for a minute!
5. If requested to move by an authorised person then MOVE!
6. Use headphones when listening to your airband radio.

Part 1
Airband Radio Receivers and Antennas

INTRODUCTION TO AIRBAND RADIO

There's been a huge explosion of interest in airband radio listening during the past twenty years. I well remember, as a young teenager, lugging my 'acorn' valved, polished wooden-boxed broadcast receiver, cleverly modified by a friend to tune the aircraft band, with its associated high and low voltage dry batteries and frame-type aerial, around airports in the 1960s. It caused quite a stir amongst the plane spotters at the time, but was an absolute pig to tune and keep tuned!

Advances in microelectronics, increasing leisure time and more disposable income have all played their part in this upsurge of interest, but by far the biggest reason is that people have been finding out just how fascinating listening to aircraft and air traffic control centres actually is! Radio receivers may now be bought for a few pounds or for many thousands, with performance from the superb to the er . . . well, not very good. Never have the airbands – yes; there *are* more than one – been so easily accessible, and with such a choice of sophisticated equipment, as they are today. And, there's no heavy batteries to hump either!

Before you rush off to purchase that military-looking 'Aircraft Band' radio receiver with the multipurpose knobs, dials and synchronised flashing lights, in the bike shop window, pause for a moment. What do you actually know about aeronautical mobile radio? Enough to walk confidently into a shop and purchase exactly what you want? In many books on airband radio listening, the newcomer is ordered to buy a 'cheap 'n' cheerful' receiver until such time as they discover that they 'like' what they're doing, and can then go out and buy a much more expensive one. They, of course, never say what to do with the first receiver, nor where to find the cash for the second!

Buy Cheap – Sell High!

In my humble opinion this is completely the *wrong* way of going about things. If your first buy is a cheap airband receiver, then you're never even going to hear most of the VHF airband, much less be able to develop an informed opinion about how interesting (or otherwise!) airband listening really is. You can't pick up the airport ATIS transmissions, nor listen to an incoming aircraft being handed-over from En-route ATC to airport Approach Control. You won't be able to follow the aeroplane's vectoring onto the ILS, or pick up the Aerodrome Controller as he or she gives permission for the aircraft to land.

Neither will you be able to follow that aircraft along the runway, off into a taxiway and back to its stand if all you can do is blindly swish the tuning knob of your 'cheap' airband receiver up and down the band, searching for a signal, *any* signal!

When hunting for a suitable airband receiver, you're looking for a special tool for a particular job. The choice is vast and confusing. Within every price range there are good and bad receivers; the trick is to acquire as much knowledge about airband radio as you can, and then apply it when making your choice.

In this part of the Handbook, I will be explaining High Frequency, Very High Frequency and Ultra High Frequency radio transmissions, which give us the HF, VHF and UHF airbands. I will also discuss airband radio receiver features, such as memories, scanning etc. and end with a survey of available radio receivers. But first let's obtain as much information about airband radio as we can, before spending any money on a receiver.

THE VERY HIGH FREQUENCY (VHF) AIRCRAFT BAND

As this is by far the most popular airband, and easily the most accessible, with an amazing variety of receivers to choose from, I'll deal with it first, as a complete subject before moving onto the UHF and HF airbands.

Aeronautical Mobile Radio is ground-based radio navigation devices (*navaids*) and radio telephony (R/T) messages between the pilot of an aircraft, the aircraft itself and a ground station, such as an airport or Air Traffic Control Centre. This radio communication takes place for two basic reasons: aircraft safety and navigation. It is the method by which Air Traffic Control deliver their messages and instructions to the pilots.

The VHF Aircraft Band starts at 108mHz – which is where the FM broadcast band on a domestic receiver ends – and goes up to 137mHz, although the United Kingdom is still only using 136mHz as the upper limit. The band may be split into sub-bands. The area 108–118mHz is allocated to radio-navigation aids, such as VOR beacons and Instrument Landing Systems. There's nothing much of interest to hear in this sub-band, unless you're fond of whistles, pops, sawing noises and Morse code, of course. Many people evidently are, myself included.

Most radio telephony (R/T) takes place between 118–136mHz, where there is a great deal to interest plane spotters. Airports tend to cluster around the bottom end of this sub-band, between 118–125mHz; while En-route Air Traffic Control stay at the top end, 125–136mHz. Of course, there are exceptions to this. The modulation used is always AM, and communication is by the *Simplex* method; which means both stations using the same frequency. One listens, the other transmits. Diagram 1 summarises this information.

Frequency Channels

The VHF civil airband is channelised for ease of use. There are 200 navigation channels between 108–118mHz, spaced at 50kHz intervals. There are some 720 possible R/T channels available between 118–136mHz, although they aren't all in use at the same time, thank goodness! VHF radio is essentially a short-range, line-of-sight communication mode and the transmitting aerial has to be 'looking' at the receiving antenna for good communication to take place. This is not a problem for the airport and aircraft. With the aeroplane's height advantage it can 'see' the airport's antennas from a long way.

The problems start when we airband listeners try to listen to an airport from our homes. Any obstruction between the terminal's aerials and our receiving antennas will at best weaken the signal but, more often than not, block it all together. What normally happens is that you can pick up the aircraft talking to airport ATC, but not the controller's replies, which is slightly frustrating. However, as we shall see later, there's much we can do to improve reception from home, and other 'tricks of the trade' for those who haven't yet paid their dues. As around 80% to 90% of your airband listening *will* take place from home, it's well worth while doing everything you can to improve reception there.

AIRBAND RADIO RECEIVER FEATURES

What follows is a summary of basic airband radio receiver features, what they do and how they can improve your listening. Some receivers will have a few of these facilities: others may have all of them. You have to choose which features you want and which you can live without.

Common Receiver Features

All radio receivers share the following features; they're just as important to a domestic broadcast bands receiver as they are to one dedicated for the VHF airband. They concern the actual performance of the receiver, how 'good' or 'bad' it will be for the job in hand.

AIR-7, R535S, HF225, AOR3000, R537S, Saisho MC600. Dee-Comm Scanning antenna (background)

Frequency Coverage

After reading the above, you'll now know that the frequency range of the VHF Aircraft Band starts at 108mHz and ends at 136mHz. So any potential receiver you have in mind *must* cover that range – completely, without any gaps. Some airband receivers lop off the first part of the band, between 108–118mHz so, if you own such a receiver, you won't be able to listen to the Navaids sub-band. However, lots of people can live with this. Other receivers end their airband coverage at 135mHz (don't ask me why). Whatever airband you decide you would like to hear you must ensure that the receiver's frequency coverage is adequate. A list of *all* airbands together with their frequency ranges can be found in Radiodatabase 7.

Receiver Sensitivity

If there's one question I tire of answering at an airport, it's 'And how far away can your radio pick up aeroplanes, mister?' I know what these people really mean; they, like most un-informed opinion, base a receiver's ability to capture distant stations as a measure of the radio's 'goodness'. Because it hears something distant, it must be a 'good' receiver. 'Distance', 'goodness' etc. are relative terms anyway. A receiver's sensitivity is just part of a much wider issue concerning its usefulness, and taken in isolation is totally misleading! You may have the world's most sensitive radio receiver, but if it doesn't have good *Selectivity* and *Stability*, or even a decent antenna, then it's all but useless.

In the specifications listing, which usually accompanies advertisements for airband radio receivers in magazines etc., sensitivity is quoted as so many microvolts for 10 dB S/N, e.g:

$$1\mu V - 10 \text{ dB S/N Ratio}$$

Simply, 1 microvolt (μV) sensitivity is very good: anything below 1, such as $0.5\mu V$, is excellent. But remember: sensitivity is only part of a bigger picture, and must never be seen as the whole issue.

Selectivity

I promise not to involve you in any further complex receiver specifications! Selectivity is simply the receiver's ability to reject unwanted signals; 'unwanted' meaning anything you're not actually tuned to. If you're monitoring a frequency of 124.000mHz, then you don't want the radio station next door on 124.025mHz leaking through on top.

Cheap airband receivers, the ones with airband 'thrown in' with various broadcast bands, are particularly prone to selectivity problems. You could be tuned to a frequency of, say 120.000mHz, but any transmissions between 118–124mHz (that's 240 R/T channels!) could be coming through loud and clear on your selected frequency. Often more than one at a time too!

Wait; it gets worse. Where these 'cheaper' sets often have Public Service Bands as well as airband, you could have a real problem identifying exactly what it is you're listening to – a yacht, a local taxi, the Gas Board or sometimes, even an aircraft!

Stability

The final part of my Performance Triptych is the receiver's stability; its ability to stay exactly on frequency without drifting off. My first-ever airband radio receiver had all the stability of a plateful of jelly on board a yacht in the Bay of Biscay in a Force-Ten blow!

Stability is obviously important. It is hardest to achieve in mechanical VFO tuning, which the majority of domestic, broadcast bands receivers with airband, and some dedicated airband radios have as their method of tuning in stations.

It is relatively easy to ensure with quartz crystal or synthesised frequency control – more of which later. However, nothing is for nothing; crystal and frequency synthesis do cost more than the simple mechanical VFO, but at least you're ensured spot-on frequency accuracy, often better than 0.1% with a quartz rock, and even better with synthesis.

SUMMARY

A good airband receiver will be reasonably sensitive, very selective and stable. It will cover those frequency ranges you're interested in without gaps. Being at an airport, airfield, airshow – or even just watching gliders in the distance – without airband radio is exactly like watching the television with the sound switched off (who said that's the only way to watch it?). You will be able to see but not hear. Similarly, having an 'unsuitable' airband receiver – and when you've finished reading this part of the Handbook, *you* will be able to define 'unsuitable' – is actually worse than not having one at all! It will give you a totally misleading idea of what airband radio is about.

THE CONTROLS AND FACILITIES

Tuning Arrangements. The VFO

Starting with the controls common to *all* airband receivers, I'll then move on to the more exotic. The Prime control is the tuning knob, which connects to a mechanical VFO, although this is rapidly heading for extinction! This is the control which decides what stations we listen to by altering the received frequency. It is linked by either cogs and gears, or often pulleys and string to a pointer moving in front of a printed dial or scale which tells you (approximately) what frequency you're tuned to. The length of the tuning dial/scale varies enormously, from around a foot to as little as an inch! Obviously, the bigger the tuning scale/dial, then the easier the radio will be to set onto a precise frequency. Some broadcast-with-airband receivers do actually achieve a fair rate of tuning accuracy, others are abysmal!

One thing you must *never* do is to confuse selectivity with the length of the tuning dial. The two are *not* linked in any way at all. Long tuning ranges may make it easier to tune, but are absolutely no help at all in refusing to accept signals from outside of where the receiver is presently tuned.

Crystal Control

Another way of tuning an airbands receiver is to use a quartz crystal – or 'rock', as airband enthusiasts call it. With a mechanical VFO, the tuning knob is turned back and forth which varies the frequency of the receiver (VFO stands for Variable Frequency Oscillator). With crystal control, each quartz rock is cut to a precise frequency, and when you want to listen to that frequency you simply select that particular crystal. Of course, this does mean that you need one crystal for *every* frequency you want to listen to; and, as there are potentially 700+ frequency channels, working at an average cost of £4.75 per crystal, that's an incredible £3,325!

In practice nothing like this astronomical figure is reached. What usually happens is that the plane spotter has a couple of crystals for his local airport, maybe two more for his local En-route ATC frequencies, and then a couple for airshows, or gliders.

Frequency Synthesis

The difficulty and expense of producing a high quality, mechanical VFO is well known in the radio industry, as is the cost to the buyer of quartz crystals. What was needed was something which at least equalled, and preferably bettered, the stability of quartz, yet was much easier to manufacture than the mechanical VFO. And so Frequency Synthesis was invented. Basically, synthesis uses a single, very stable and accurate 'lump' of quartz as a reference by which frequency is synthetically generated using various electronic and timing devices. What this means is that an airband radio receiver (or any other receiver) employing frequency synthesis can cover just about any frequency with astonishing accuracy and stability, at a tiny fraction of the cost of the equivalent quartz crystals. Of course, once you delve into the region of digital electronics as employed in frequency synthesis, then the world really does become your oyster, as this technology has not only made possible radio receivers of unparalleled accuracy, but also provided a gateway for advanced features such as memory stores, frequency scanning and priority channels.

Digital Display Of Frequency

One of the problems with a VFO is that if you want to listen to something at the top of the airband, then you have to physically wind the dial pointer from one end of the scale right up to the other. With frequency synthesis, any frequency can be accessed immediately, simply by requesting it. So, instead of the usual pointer and dial mechanism of the VFO, synthesised receivers use Direct Digital Frequency Display (DDFD).

Instead of having to interpret where a dial pointer is in relation to the airband, DDFD tells you exactly, often to three decimal places, where you are. The most obvious advantage is when searching for a station, such as an airport control tower, or approach frequency. Instead of moving a VFO pointer to approximately the right place, and then swishing it up and down searching for the signal, you can simply look up the required frequency (for instance in the VHF Radiodatabase in this Handbook), tap it into the receiver and there you are: instantly too!

Synthesised receivers usually show the frequency on a Liquid Crystal Display (LCD), just like those used by present-day electronic pocket calculators. Early forms of synthesised radios, such as the SIGNAL R532S, used LED displays – Light Emitting Diodes, which are numbers which glow, usually red.

Squelch

No; not the sound your airband receiver makes when it's dropped into a muddy puddle! Squelch is the control which cuts out the background 'white noise', the hissing heard between radio telephony messages. It works by temporarily reducing the receiver's apparent sensitivity, and is usually a rotary control, much like the 'volume' knob. Turning it anti-clockwise reduces its effect, until a point is reached where the squelch is fully open. When fully clockwise, only the strongest signals will break through the squelch threshold.

The correct setting for the squelch is to turn it fully off (so you can hear the background hiss) and then advance it until the white noise just disappears. One sure sign of an airband receiver being pushed beyond its design limits is to note that the squelch control is permanently off! In any case, most of the advanced receiver features, such as frequency scanning and memory searching, rely on the squelch control being on. They will not work *at all* with the squelch off!

Memories Are Made Of This

Thanks to the technology which gave us frequency synthesis, we now have such useful features as memory cells. These are simply pieces of circuitry inside the receiver which allow us to store numbers within them; such as a radio frequency. Early radios had just the one: the AOR1000 handheld Scanning receiver holds the current record with one thousand memories. But the usual range is anywhere between ten and a hundred. The receiver will 'remember' these numbers and, when you want to recall a particular frequency, you only need to give the location number (address) of the individual memory cell. An internal battery supplies power to the memory circuits which means that the receiver still remembers all the numbers it has stored, even when the power has been switched off.

Instead of tapping-in, or dialling-up Airways, Approach, Radar, Ground and Tower ATC frequencies on your airband receiver for all of your favourite airports and airfields, you can enter them all once into the receiver's memory cells, and recall them whenever you want. However, useful as this feature undoubtedly is, memories can offer much more than this; but, before going any further, let's look at scanning.

Frequency Scanning

To avoid confusion from here on, 'scanning', with a small 's', refers to the receiver's ability automatically to search frequencies or memories. 'Scanning' with a capital 'S' refers to a particular type of receiver, *not* a receiver feature.

Be warned! This is a deadly simple concept which can have you tearing your hair out when it goes wrong! Frequency scanning is just that: the receiver tunes itself, up or down the band very quickly, often checking around twenty channels a second, and having a very brief peek at each frequency in passing. What it actually does when it discovers a radio signal depends on which option you've chosen. At its most basic, the scan will simply stop when it runs into a radio transmission above the squelch threshold – the squelch *must* be closed before a scan can start.

Variations of the scan can be: receiver stops the scan on acquiring a signal, but re-starts on touching a key, or, the receiver pauses until the 'carrier' disappears, when the receiver then commences scanning again, until the next signal. When the scan eventually reaches the top of the band, it will either pause, then recommence coming back down again, or scroll around to the bottom starting the scan upwards depending on whether you initiated an 'upwards' or 'downwards' scan pattern. 'Carrier', in this case, is the radio signal encountered by the scan.

What's so dreadful about that, then? Ah, but on most receivers with scanning facilities, you can specify many conditions for the scan. You can ask it to scan in certain sized 'jumps', such as 5, 12.5, 25 or 50kHz; or in a particular direction. You can preset frequency limits to the scan, such as 'search between this lower limit; and that upper limit'. You may also tell the scan to ignore totally certain frequencies, or 'Lock-out', as it is called. And it's when you get all these options around your ears that the fun starts, and the receiver disappears up its own antenna! You can often see this effect on the spectator terraces at an airport, where you'll observe someone with a huge headache frantically ripping the batteries out of a receiver, desperately trying to reset it.

Memory Scan – Memory Search

Actually, I don't rate frequency scanning very highly. It seems a trifle silly to me to let the receiver blindly wander all over the place looking for signals. The trick is to *know* where the signals will be; put your receiver into the right area and then wait for it to appear. Of far more use is memory scanning, where all the frequencies you stored inside the receiver's memory are searched for activity. On finding a signal, the scan will park the receiver on that memory channel.

Priority Memory Channel

This is a particular memory location dedicated to the Priority function. Anything stored in this location will be checked twice a second (varies according to make, of course) and, when activity is detected, the receiver immediately re-tunes itself to the priority channel, from wherever and whatever it was doing before the radio signal was detected. Very useful.

CHOOSING AN AIRBAND RECEIVER

Before you contemplate a purchase, exactly what are your require-ments? Do you want a handheld, base/mobile, base only, dedicated airband, civil, military or Scanning receiver. Would you be better off with a Scanner? Don't wait until you get to the shop door before making your mind up, you may well find yourself walking out with what the salesperson thinks you ought to have! And you can't blame them if *you* can't decide!

Scanners

Let's deal with the business of a dedicated airband versus a Scanning receiver first. A Scanning receiver is much like a dedicated airband receiver, except that it will cover many frequency ranges, rather than just the one or two. Typically, a Scanning receiver may cover something like: 60–950mHz continuously; or 66–88, 108–174 and 406–512mHz in three ranges. Scanning receivers tend to have the majority of receiver features I've discussed so far, such as memories, scanning of frequency and memory, direct digital readout etc.

To sum this up succinctly. *You can always listen to the civil/military airbands on a Scanner: that's ALL you CAN listen to on a dedicated airband receiver!*

Mobile Receivers

Mobile receivers are fairly large (compared to handhelds), and require 12 volts DC to operate, which can be supplied either by a mains power supply unit or from a car battery. They don't normally come fitted with an aerial. Being designed for car use, it's expected that you will take care of the antenna requirements. A few years ago, it was true to say that mobile receivers had more facilities than handheld receivers; however, except in a very few cases, this is no longer true.

Of course you can use a base/mobile receiver portable when out, such as at an airport, airfield or airshow etc. but it's not easy. You've normally got to provide a portable 12 volts, and an external aerial, but it can be done. These receivers connect to external antennas without too many problems.

Base Station Receivers

Base station receivers – which are usually Scanners – have the space and scope for many extra features, such a Panaramic Display of received signals, more memory and scan options etc. They have more input/output connections than handhelds, for items such as tape recorders, external aerials and even remote control by a computer. Base receivers are usually powered by mains electricity, but increasingly they're now fitted with a 12 volt option as well.

Their selectivity, sensitivity and overall performance is generally of a very high order indeed. They are primarily designed to work from the home environment, on an external aerial (unlike handhelds – see later). Base station receivers are usually the most expensive types of radios because of the extra facilities and performance standard they offer.

Handheld Receivers

As their name implies, handhelds are designed for hand-portable use. Recent trends have added more and more features to these receivers, particularly the handheld Scanning radios, where their instruction manuals are currently running to something around 30 pages! Compare that to the four pages of my SIGNAL R532S instruction manual. Handhelds run on their own internal batteries, and with LCD displays as opposed to the older, LEDs, battery life is much improved.

It is important for you to understand the philosophy of the handheld receiver, which is, a self-contained portable radio designed to work with its own power source *and aerial*. It's this last bit where people can come to grief. The manufacturers of handheld receivers (quite rightly) assume that it's going to be used with the antenna they supply. The internal amplification of the receiver's front-end (where the radio signal enters the receiver via the aerial) is boosted considerably to increase the efficiency of the rather inefficient rubber helical, or chromium whip antenna.

Everything's fine – just as long as you *are* actually using the manufacturer's aerial. The problems start when you attach the handheld receiver to an external antenna. Coupled to such an aerial, the front-end amplification then becomes far too much, and the receiver runs into selectivity problems – the scan suddenly stopping for no apparent reason, or two stations appearing on the same channel are all indicative of this unwanted condition.

When people are looking for an airband receiver, they often want something which will cover *all* the situations they envisage, such as home listening, in the car and wandering around an airport.

The natural choice for such a receiver is the handheld. It's small enough to carry around, and may be propped up on the desk at home, or laid on the car's dashboard when mobile. But as I've already said, handhelds are *not* designed for use with external antennas.

This is why I have a handheld receiver, for airport visits, *and* a mobile receiver for use in the car and at home. Although even a mobile receiver isn't one hundred percent happy working in the home either! The ideal (assuming that you've got Greek shipping connections) is a Base, Mobile *and* a Handheld!

OTHER RECEIVER TYPES

Dedicated airband receivers are no-compromise machines, with everything crafted towards the end goal of listening to a particular airband. Such receivers as produced by WIN and the SIGNAL Corporation have been designed by aviation enthusiasts in the first place, and this is reflected in their performance and ease of use. Dedicated airband receivers will nearly always out-perform all but the most expensive Scanning receivers, but only on the airbands, of course.

Broadcast With Airband

These receivers are around the cheapest you'll find, ranging in price from around £10 to £40. They are basically domestic radios with airband 'tossed in' and, as such, they come under the less stringent requirements of cheap, mass-produced broadcast receivers. They are most certainly *not* designed to cope with high RF fields, or very precise frequency setting. Performance varies from barely adequate (with restrictions) to the downright appalling! I have explained how to get the best from this type of receiver in Part 4.

Pseudo-Communications Receivers

Pseudo because they aren't really! Much like a Mini will never be a Porsche, even though both are motor cars. A true communications receiver is an expensive piece of gear which offers many frequency ranges and modes, and has very exacting demands to meet. These 'pretend' communication receivers can be splendidly impressive – huge tuning dials labelled with exotica such as: 'Weather Satellites', 'Ship-To-Shore Radio' and 'Space Band'. Masses of knobs and lights, massive casings with lots of plastic chrome and really emotive names, such as: 'World Zapper', or 'The Juggernaut Ocean Stomper'! Oh; you've seen them too?

Apart from the usual Long Wave (LW), Medium Wave (MW) and VHF FM broadcast bands, they cover many Short Wave (HF) radio frequencies, and a few other VHF bands as well as the VHF civil airband. Yes; they *are* impressive to look at, and I'll put my hand up and admit to once buying one. Oh, alright then, a couple. The trouble is, they're built to exactly the same standard as domestic receivers, with mechanical VFOs, and will simply not come up to the standard you've a right to expect having bought yourself a 'communications receiver'. However; all is not lost. These types of receiver – thanks to their long tuning scales or dials – can be successfully modified (externally) for airband listening.

There are a few VHF-type 'Pseudo-Communications Receivers' around. They offer sections of various VHF bands, such as 66–80, 108–140 and 150–200mHz. To add versimilitude to their communications receiver pretensions, some of them even forsake the broadcast bands altogether.

Often, on the VHF Public Service Bands, narrow-band communication modes are employed, such as Narrow Band Frequency Modulation (NBFM), so that more stations can be 'fitted in' to the available space. Ordinary, broadcast FM is wide-band FM, occupying a lot of space on the band. Part of the trouble with these receivers is that they employ the same wide-band IF filter required by broadcast band FM for receiving narrow-band communications; which is unsuitable, and causes very poor selectivity.

Finally, such receivers usually allow coverage of the VHF airband by simply extending the tuning range of the VHF FM broadcast band. Nothing wrong with this, except that, for VHF FM listening, the FM mode is used: the VHF airband requires AM. Such receivers will only allow you to hear the VHF airband through the FM demodulator and, of course, this is totally unsuitable for the VHF airband!

ACCESSORIES

Anything which doesn't actually come with the receiver when you buy it is an accessory. With that in mind, it's always wise to check exactly what does come with the radio and what you will be left to buy after-wards. You can often tell a 'good' receiver simply by the accessories which come with it. An example of this is the superb AOR1000 Scanner which comes complete with case, carrying strap, belt clip, flexible, helically-wound antenna (a 'rubber ducky' in airband-speak!), Nickel Cadmium (NiCad) battery set and a mains charger/power supply for charging and powering the radio when at home.

Nickel Cadmium Rechargeable Batteries (NiCads)

The most obvious accessory is an external aerial so that the airbands may be listened to from home. I am covering aerials in their own section, so I'll leave them for now. An investment which will repay you many times over is two sets of Nickel Cadmium (NiCad) rechargeable batteries; one on, and one 'in the wash', and a suitable charger for them. The AA size NiCads are now virtually as cheap as the more heavily advertised manganese/alkaline, disposable versions. NiCads can be recharged around a thousand times – I've had some of mine for years, easily exceeding 1000 charges, and they're still going strong.

You may be told that a NiCad is 'Quick-Charge', although it's really the battery charger which decides this, not the battery itself. When exhausted, such NiCads may be recharged to full capacity in anything between half-an-hour to around four hours. Normal (non-quick) charge time is sixteen hours.

It is very important to know exactly how long your NiCads need for a full charge, as exceeding this time, e.g. 'over-charging', can damage them. You won't be doing a 'quick-charge' NiCad any favours by leaving it charging for sixteen hours instead of one!

A final point to remember about NiCad batteries; their working voltage is slightly less than their equivalent brothers, e.g. a manganese/

alkaline AA size, 'throwaway' battery is 1.5 volts, four of which makes up a common receiver operating voltage of 6 volts. But AA NiCads are 1.2 volts: four of them add up to 4.8 volts, not six. On some airband receivers, this can be a problem so, before investing in a set (or two) of Nickel Cadmium rechargeable batteries, make certain that your receiver can work on this reduced voltage level.

In my experience, if a receiver is not suitable for NiCads, the instruction manual will tell you so. If no mention is made of NiCads, then it's usually safe to use them. If in any doubt, ask the assistant in the shop when buying your receiver, which is yet another good reason for not buying your airband radio from the local supermarket!

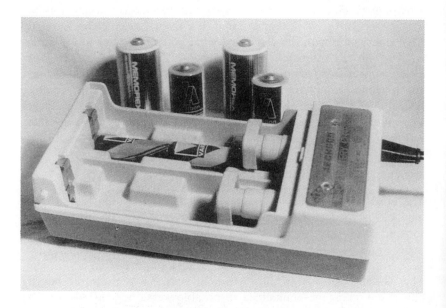

NiCad battery charger plus range of rechargeable batteries

Tape Recorders and VOX

In your early days as a plane spotter, when subjects like ATC and Oceanic airband radio are still new to you, it's a good idea to tape record these types of message so that you can replay them a few times, going over the difficult bits. Any type of tape recorder will do, but most people find the ease and convenience of cassette recorders better suited to their needs. You can get a maximum of an hour's recording time per side when using a C120-type cassette.

You could of course simply set the recorder going and leave it, but this means searching through the tape afterwards, looking for the signals. A better option is to either buy a cassette tape recorder with a built-in VOX switch, or add a VOX switching unit to an existing recorder. Either way, the results will be identical. The VOX – or Voice Operated Switching as it is known – only starts the tape recorder when a voice appears on the frequency the radio is presently tuned to. It doesn't have to be a voice, in fact *sound* operated switching would be a better description, as it's sound which trips the VOX circuit, not just voices.

Your receiver will need a squelch control, which must be ON. When a radio signal breaks through the squelch's threshold, the VOX switch trips and the tape machine starts recording. About a second after the squelch closes again, the recorder stops, and waits for the next signal. The end result is around two to three hours of real-time airband radio messages compressed into about half an hour's continuous replay on the VOX-switched tape recording.

I use a microcassette recorder with built-in VOX. It's a Saisho, model MC600, available from Dixons. It has two speeds as well as the VOX switching. With a 30-minute tape on its slowest speed, it gives me an hour's recording time. It's very small, slipping easily into a pocket, so I can take it with me on airport visits etc. where I also use it for its primary function of an audio notebook.

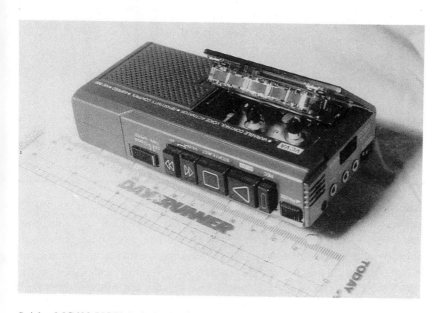

Saisho MC600 VOX-Switched Microcassette recorder

Headphones & Earphones

At airports such as Gatwick, Heathrow and Manchester, the cacophony from 30 or 40 airband receivers can often be quite deafening! Therefore, headphones are dual purpose: they not only make it much easier for you to hear the ATC transmissions you're interested in, they also protect your ears from aircraft and other noise. Ordinary stereo 'walkman' type headphones are more than adequate, although you may need to change the plug from the 3.5mm stereo to a 3.5mm MONO jack – Diagram 2 shows you how – otherwise you'll find that the sound may only come through either the left or the right earpiece.

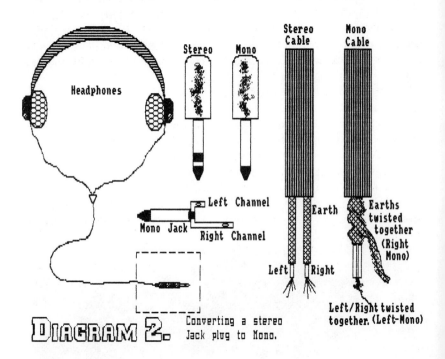

Converting a stereo Jack plug to Mono.

Odds 'n' Ends

Another fairly vital accessory for airband radio listening is information. Although I've given you enough HF, VHF and UHF airband frequencies to keep you out of mischief for many a day, my lists are not definitive. In the Appendices you'll find a list of books and magazines which will provide you with a great deal of additional information regarding radio frequency allocations, basic radio techniques and magazines which include a regular 'Airband Column'.

A carrying case for your receiver is a wise investment, and the heavier it is the more protection it will provide. No matter how careful you are something always seems to happen. I take very good care of my receivers, yet I've dropped them both quite a few times now, and once even ran over my SIGNAL R537S with my wheelchair, which says something fairly important about that particular radio as, apart from a few dents and a broken plastic battery cover, the receiver still works fine!

AIRBAND RADIO RECEIVERS: A SUMMARY

The cheap broadcast-with-airband receiver will undoubtedly pick up aircraft band radio transmissions. They cost around £10–£30, although prices do vary widely. You may have got the impression (can't imagine why) that I don't really like this type of airband receiver. I fully accept that for some people this will be their only access to the VHF airband, and it is often said that *any* receiver is better than none, not that I subscribe to this, of course.

I have explained in detail the sort of problems these receivers can encounter. Some of them can be overcome; and, just as long as you remember their limitations and operate the receiver within them, things shouldn't be too bad; although by using such a receiver, you're never going to be able to enjoy the full benefits, and the powerful learning potential of the VHF airband. In my own personal experience, the Steepletone range seems to be 'quite good', which is as far as you'll get me to go.

Buying a dedicated airband receiver is a major decision, as you're going to commit yourself to listening to the one (or two) band(s), with no chance of expanding the frequency coverage without starting over again. And, as I've already said, we have to get it right first time or it may turn into a very expensive business.

However, such a receiver is a no-compromise machine, designed to do the one task. Every dedicated airband receiver I've used has performed absolutely superbly, and given me much pleasure, as well as teaching me a great deal about Air Traffic Control, and airport operations etc. Dedicated airband receivers start at around £60–£80, and can go up to thousands! An average price is around £200. A mere £250 gets you the 'Rolls-Royce' of dedicated airband receivers – the SIGNAL R535S. If you're a dedicated plane spotter then you'll want the best.

For those who want more than the civil and military airbands, there is the phenomenal range of Scanning receivers which cover just about every frequency from DC to light waves! As with all receivers, price is a very good guide. Quality costs. There are many Scanning receivers around which do not cover the civil and/or the military airbands; their price is usually a giveaway. As their potential use is limited, the asking price reflects this. An average Scanner will set you back around £250–£350. And remember that you can listen to the civil and military airbands on a Scanner too.

For ease and portability, a handheld receiver, which is self-contained with its own internal batteries and aerial, takes some beating. It is light, packed with features and can be slipped easily into a coat pocket; just the thing for wandering around an airport or airfield. Both dedicated airband and Scanning receivers can be obtained in handheld versions. But remember what I said earlier about using external antennas on handhelds, particularly in areas of relatively high signal strength.

A mobile/base receiver is not so easy to manage when you are out and about, however it fits into the car and home environment better than a handheld. Aerial choice is up to you, and, as you'll see later, there's much you can do with such a receiver as a 'remote monitoring station.' Average price is £200.

If your budget won't run to a new dedicated airbands receiver or a Scanner, remember the secondhand market. Magazines, such as *Shortwave Magazine*, *Ham Radio Today* and the new and very exciting magazine dedicated to the scanning receiver enthusiast, *Scanners International*, which comes as a 'freebie' in *Ham Radio Today* as well as CB Citizen Band magazines. Incidentally, I write the monthly 'Civil Airband' column, so it *must* be good! Many of these magazines offer free reader's advertisements; so not only will you be looking in the right place, it won't cost you anything to advertise your needs either.

And finally. When you've acquired your 'new' receiver, for heaven's sake; *READ THE INSTRUCTION MANUAL THOROUGHLY FIRST*. Eight out of ten phone calls, concerning receiver problems, to the shops of suppliers could be answered by the caller simply reading the instruction manual *before* telephoning.

HF AIRBAND RADIO

Ultra High Frequency Airband

The Ultra High Frequency (UHF) Airband is a military airband, and as such is outside the scope of this Handbook. Civil aviation also makes use of frequencies in the UHF range. The airport Air Traffic Control Officer, known as the Ground Movement Controller (GMC), uses UHF Radio Telephony (R/T) to communicate with the airport's service and emergency vehicles. As I've gone into explicit details of 'Ground's' work in Part 2, you can read about UHF radio there. By the way, these

UHF transmissions from 'Ground' are not the same thing as 'Company Transmissions'.

High Frequency Radio

VHF and UHF radio transmissions, as we now know, are essentially short-range, line-of-sight. Due to the curvature of the earth, VHF aircraft radio telephony transmissions are restricted to a maximum range of around 200 miles. Ground station emissions cover considerably less than this, depending on their surroundings. When over-flying land in the UK and Europe, an aircraft is never far from an ATC radio service, so VHF frequencies work fine. VHF is also used to keep track of exactly where an aircraft is at any one time, either by ATC talking to the pilot, or a navigation aid, such as a VOR beacon 'talking' to the aircraft. (VOR beacons also work at VHF.)

Why HF Radio?

Over the North Atlantic Ocean, things are a whole lot different. Two hundred miles out from the coast and an aircraft's three VHF boxes cannot be used. Control of flights on the North Atlantic Track system (NATS) within the Shanwick Ocean Control Area is from Atlantic House, the home of Shanwick Oceanic Air Traffic Control Centre, which is near Prestwick airport in Ayrshire, Scotland. For most of its journey across the sea, the aircraft will be out of range of VHF radio telephony communications. *Shanwick Oceanic*, as it is known, needs to talk with the pilots of aircraft flying over the Atlantic. What it needs to talk about, we'll see later. Because of the distances involved, VHF radio isn't going to work, so air traffic control use High Frequency (HF) radio, what used to be called Short Wave radio.

What Is HF Radio?

HF radio behaves in a very different way to VHF. It is not restricted to 'line-of-sight'. HF radio waves can travel many thousands of miles in the right circumstances, with the radio waves arriving via reflections from an area of ionised gas in the upper atmosphere – the 'Skip' wave.

   This phenomena of an HF radio signal bouncing off the ionosphere gives it the ability to travel great distances, as multiple bounces or 'hops' can, and do take place. This is how radio amateurs are able to talk with like-minded friends around the world using short wave radio. The earth's ionosphere is constantly changing its chemico-electrical composition, and its ability to support HF radio wave reflections varies according to the time of day, the season of the year, and the geographical locations of the transmitting and receiving radio stations.

During the daytime, when there's plenty of sunlight to begin the ionisation process, higher short wave radio frequencies may be used. For example: 21050kHz is one of these 'higher' frequencies, and is a higher frequency than 2003kHz. 8086kHz is a higher frequency than 4045kHz. 5606kHz is a lower frequency than 13034kHz. Professional radio people like to use the highest HF frequency they can because long distances are covered relatively easily, and the radio signal when it arrives at its destination is of a higher quality. However, at night, when the ionisation process starts to break down, these higher frequencies cannot be used, so lower ones have to be brought into use.

The upshot of all this is, that, unlike VHF radio, where the same frequencies are used all the time for specific services, HF radio transmissions take place on a range of frequencies; some high and others low.

HF Frequency Bands

At VHF the airband is straightforward. It starts at 108mHz and runs up to 137mHz continuously. However, on HF the bands are split amongst various frequency ranges. For example, there is the 5mHz airband, the 8mHz band, the 11mHz airband etc. A list of both civil and military HF airbands is given in Radiodatabase 7. High frequency radio starts at around 2mHz – just above the medium wave range on a domestic broadcast receiver – and goes up to 30mHz. The 28mHz in between this upper and lower limit is packed solid with an eclectic cornucopia of clamouring, wailing, beeping, buzzing, whistling, singing, talking and yelling admixture of radio signals from all over the world. Somewhere in there is the airband radio signal you're looking for.

This may seem like writer's artistic licence; if you have already been fortunate (unfortunate?) to listen to the HF bands, then you'll know that the above is in no way an exaggeration! So far you have had the comparative luxury of receiving one VHF signal at a time in your airband receiver, and that on a quiet background too. HF radio is very different to VHF. It is noisy, very noisy!

Listening to the HF airbands can be, and often is, most frustrating, with a lot of money and garden space permanently tied up, and initial results for the beginner difficult. But the ultimate reward is that much higher. Unlike the VHF airband, where a receiver may be purchased for around a tenner, and airband radio transmissions, surprisingly enough, actually heard, there's no such option for an HF bands receiver – unless you fancy building your own. So spending anything between £400–£1500 for such equipment is not a decision to take lightly.

Single Sideband Radio Telephony

So far you've been listening to Amplitude Modulation – AM on the VHF/UHF airbands. HF airbands don't have this luxury. The basic bandwidth of an AM radio signal is around 6kHz, but errors of modulation level mean that the average is nearer 10kHz. What this means is that, supposing there was an HF airband just 50kHz wide, using AM would mean that only five stations would fit into the available space – 5×10kHz.

There is a method of reducing the extravagant space demanded by an AM transmission, and that's to change to Single Sideband (SSB). SSB is actually AM which has undergone major surgery. An AM radio signal consists of three parts: a lower sideband, a carrier and an upper sideband. This is why AM demands so much space. With single sideband, the carrier is entirely removed in the transmitter, along with one of the sidebands (which one is optional).

As the name suggests, only one sideband is actually transmitted; all the original power which was spread across *two* sidebands *and* a carrier is now concentrated into one sideband, which increases the radio signals' range considerably. On reception, the missing carrier is re-inserted by the electrical gubbins inside the receiver, and the sideband transmitted demodulated back into speech. The advantage of the system is that an SSB radio signal only occupies around 2kHz bandwidth instead of AM's 10. In our limited band of 50kHz, we can now have 25 SSB radio signals, instead of just the 5 AM ones.

Again, nothing is for nothing. The bit about the missing carrier being reintroduced inside the HF bands receiver should have given you a clue to what's coming next. Ordinary short wave radio receivers – the sort where, on a domestic radio set you may have the broadcast bands, LW, MW and VHF FM, and a range of short wave frequencies – *cannot* be used to resolve SSB radio signals, even though the frequency range on the domestic receiver is identical to the HF airbands. Similarly, those 'pseudo-communications' receivers I was talking about earlier, with range after range of short wave frequency bands, won't resolve SSB either.

Notice I deliberately said 'resolve', and not 'receive'? Any short wave radio receiver (which covers the appropriate frequencies, of course) can receive SSB but it cannot resolve it without either a Beat Frequency Oscillator (BFO) or a Product Detector – which both do the same job of re-inserting the missing carrier into a received SSB signal, the product detector doing it better than a BFO. Listening to an SSB signal without a BFO is virtually impossible, the speech sounding, so I'm told, like a certain Mr D. Duck Esq having a heated exchange with a Martian.

Listening to Single Sideband

The ability to listen and understand SSB transmissions is an acquired art. Chances are that when you first hear it you'll hardly understand one word in three. Don't worry, this is quite normal. People who regularly listen to SSB signals develop an ear for it, and have been known to become quite impatient with someone who hears it for the very first time. They hear perfectly, and cannot for the life of them understand how someone else cannot!

High Frequency Radio Receivers

To enable you to listen to the HF airbands, the receiver must have the correct frequency coverage and either a BFO or a product detector. The comments I made when dealing with VHF airband receivers are not only equally important here, they are doubly so. VHF airband receivers have a relatively easy life. HF receivers certainly do not, and any problem with selectivity won't just spoil the enjoyment of your new HF receiver, it will positively ruin it!

To be used for listening to HF airbands the receiver has to cover the appropriate range – 2–28mHz for *all* of the HF airbands – but do note it is not necesssary to cover them all! There is at least one home construction kit that I know of which covers the 5mHz airband and costs less than £20! But, of course, if your HF receiver does cover all the airbands, you'll always be able to locate the aircraft, ATCCs etc.

Howes DcRx HF Airband receiver kit (built)

High Frequency Communications Receivers

Expensive beasts these but, if you want the best, then this is what to aim for. They normally cover the range 500kHz to 30mHz, and have digital frequency readout, which I consider vital. Whereas on the VHF receiver most people wondered what the attenuator switch was for, on a communications receiver it will be your life-line!

It will often have various levels of attenuation, something like '10dB–20dB–30dB.' The higher the 'dB' number, then the more attenuation you're switching in, cutting down the amount of signal received. There are hundreds of very high power transmitters on the HF bands, switching in the attenuator can have literally amazing results. That aircraft position report you were struggling to listen to suddenly becomes crystal clear once the attenuator is working!

Upper or Lower?

Older receivers may have a BFO control knob on the front panel, which you will have to use to 'fine-tune' a SSB signal. Modern receivers, which use product detecting for SSB resolution, have a mode switch, which may have something like the following:

'AM – Upper Sideband – Lower Sideband – CW'

A rotary control is used to select the mode. AM speaks for itself. The choice between Upper and Lower sideband depends on which one was transmitted. For the HF airbands this will normally be *upper sideband*.

Is size important?

Communications receivers used to be great whacking things, which totally dominated a room, and took over your desk. Nowadays, they are very small (in comparison), but still larger than most VHF/UHF receivers. They don't come with an aerial, and the antenna you'll have to use will be many, many times bigger than the VHF chromium telescopic whip on your VHF/UHF airband sets. Even so, there are ways around this too – see the Aerials section. Most may be powered either by mains voltage or 12 volts, so you can take one to the airport. Prices vary widely, from around £400 up to telephone numbers! There are cheaper ways of getting onto the HF airbands, but, in the end, you'll only ever get what you pay for.

The Review section lists what I, in my very humble opinion, consider to be the best available airband receivers, Scanners and HF equipment, together with commercially available aerial and receiver kits. But don't follow my advice blindly, do some of your own reviewing and, where possible, testing too.

A Future For HF Radio?

Many people have been saying for quite a long time that, with the proliferation of communications satellites, the days of HF radio are numbered! Without doubt, a satellite communications link between, say Shanwick Oceanic at Atlantic House and an aircraft over the Atlantic Ocean would be ideal, and has much in its favour. However, although it's been promised for years, it hasn't happened yet. The aviation world is notoriously conservative where new technology affecting passenger safety is concerned; and quite rightly so.

Without doubt, it *will* happen one day. But then, the technology which provides EFIS – Electronic Flight Information System – displays on the flight deck of an aircraft, and which is just beginning to make an appearance on various aeroplanes, has been around for about twenty years already! Yes, aircraft HF radio will be replaced by satellite communications, but not for a long while yet; so buy your receiver with confidence!

Not Only But Also!

Buying an HF communications receiver may lead you into an allied hobby; that of the Short Wave Listener. These people spend their free time listening to radio signals from down the road or the other side of the world. They cover frequencies from the extremely long waves (VLF) right up to microwaves. There is a vast wealth of interesting things to hear on the HF bands, from Polar exploration teams to satellite telemetry downlinks, and from political propaganda stations, to pirate (clandestine) stations. You may hear a political coup in process, pick up a Mayday distress call from a trawler in the North Sea, and then listen to an RAF Search & Rescue Nimrod as it looks for it. There are the amateur radio stations, who mainly use SSB and Morse code, shipping, press agencies, various embassies and even Slow-Scan television, press and weather FAX stations. All extremely interesting stuff.

Listening to the HF airbands is never easy. To be consistently successful requires plenty of practice, one – or several – of the books listed in the Bibliography, and a good quality HF receiver, such as any of those in the Review section. Many receivers have features, or cover frequency ranges, you may not want. So why buy such a machine? Finally, there are several receivers which cover the whole lot! HF, VHF, UHF and even microwave bands for the latest generation of Microwave Landing Systems which are replacing the ILS.

I refuse to be blamed for your divorce when your wife/husband finds out how much you've spent on airband receivers. Haven't I tried really hard to discourage you? I'll leave this section with the Airband Listener's last request to his best friend.

'Dear old friend, promise me one last thing?'
'Of course, Old Chap, anything. Just name it'
'Please don't let my wife sell my airband receivers for what I told her I paid for them!'

AIRBAND RADIO RECEIVER REVIEWS

To attempt even a mini review of every scanner and airband receiver currently available would fill several books, much less this one. What I've tried to do is to review the most popular receivers, the ones most often seen in use at airshows, airports and other aviation events, and those favoured for use in the home. If I've missed your favourite receiver, then I'm sorry. Similarly, no conclusions should be drawn because a receiver is *not* mentioned in the review: absence is purely due to restrictions on space, and in no way should be construed as hidden criticism. All opinions expressed are, of course, entirely my own.

The receivers are split into four basic groups for ease of comparison. Group 1 are the *Dedicated* airband receivers. Group 2 *Scanning* receivers. Group 3 *HF (short wave)* receivers. Group 4 *'All-Band'* receivers (those which cover HF/VHF and UHF). I've selected at least one receiver from each group and subjected it to a 'road-test'; using it for airband radio listening only. Not all of the receivers slot neatly into a particular category; in such cases I've chosen to group them by their primary function. Prices were abstracted from current magazine adverts, and represent the average.

Obviously the scanning and short wave receivers enable a listener to hear much more than various airband radio messages. For all the receivers I tested, I used them only on the airbands, and all comments made relate to their airband radio performance only.

Buying

You wouldn't really buy a new car mail order, nor purchase a new single-lens reflex camera system from a door-to-door salesman. What you would do is go to a garage or photographic shop because, quite naturally, before parting with (often) quite a lot of money, you want advice, information, back-up in the unlikely event that a problem should arise; or, in other words, you want security for your investment.

Buying a very specialised item, such as an airband radio receiver or Scanner, requires exactly the same amount of caution as a new car or camera. So why buy from the local supermarket or butcher? Buying from the specialised dealers brings you that indispensable peace of mind. You'll be talking to and dealing with experts, who will not only dissuade you from purchasing 'a lemon', (not that they'd even stock such a thing) but will also ensure that, whatever you do buy, you'll know how to get the utmost from it. Is all that buyer's security worth sacrificing for the sake of mere pennies: no contest really, is it?

GROUP 1. DEDICATED AIRBAND RADIO RECEIVERS

SIGNAL R535 VHF/UHF

Type	Base/mobile, synthesised
Frequency range	108–143mHz. 220–399.975mHz
Channel steps	5/10/25/50 & 100 kHz
Sensitivity	0.32μV-VHF/0.46μV-UHF 12dB SINAD
Display	Back-lit, digital LCD
Memories	60
Lock-out	Yes
Scan type	Selectable lower-upper frequency limits, selectable channel steps
Scan speed	12 channels per second
Search	Yes, with lock-out
Power source	External 12 volts (internal option)
Aerial	Internal chrome whip, two external antenna sockets: SO239 & BNC
Modes	AM only
Squelch	Yes
Price	£250

A dual-band, dedicated airbands receiver covering the full VHF civil and UHF military airbands. It is a model of simplicity to use, and yet extremely powerful as well. I can't think of many other receivers where I can mention simplicity and powerful in the same sentence! There are three basic modes of operation – Manual, Seek and Scan. Frequency setting and memory channel selection is by moving an underline cursor beneath the digit to be changed, and then stepping up or down: it really is as simple as that.

In Use

I have used the R535S at home and mobile, whilst en-route to Manchester airport. Connecting the R535 to my VHF/UHF mobile scanning aerial, I set off for Manchester.

I could hear aircraft talking to Manchester Approach control, on frequency 119.400mHz all the way over, of course, but it wasn't until I reached the summit of Woodhead Pass on my trans-Pennine crossing that I could begin to hear the Approach controller directly. That's pretty impressive for a distance of over 30 miles, and still lots of intervening high ground between my car's antenna and the aerials at Manchester Airport.

R535 Summary

The R535S is a Mobile/Base and, with the appropriate kit, is a portable radio which offers very powerful features. You need to supply an external aerial of some type, and of course the necessary 12 volts. Power may be from a car battery, using the supplied lead, a mains power pack, or the special Nickel Cadmium battery pack, which comes with the carrying case, and rubber, helical antenna in the portable pack. Both these latter items are optional extras. The receiver remained remarkably free from Squelch Chatter – an irritating business when mobile, where a weak station continuously breaks into and out of the receiver's squelch control, producing an annoying audible chattering noise. This receiver has a socket on the backplate for connection to a computer's RS232 port.

Having tested it in a mobile and base station configuration, listening to the civil and military airbands, the only thing I can't understand is how Lowe Electronics who are, incidentally the sole UK importers for SIGNAL receivers, can possibly sell it for an astonishing £250!

WIN 108 VHF

Type	Handheld, synthesised
Frequency range	108–143mHz
Channel steps	25kHz
Sensitivity	0.4µV 12dB SINAD
Display	Back-lit, digital LCD
Memories	20 in two banks of 10 (A/B)
Lock-out	Yes
Scan type	Selectable lower/upper limits simple frequency scan with delay or hold
Scan speed	1mHz in 5 seconds
Search	Yes, with lock-out, speed 10 CPS
Power source	6V – ×4 AA NiCad/dry batteries, or external PSU
Aerial	Rubber covered helical, BNC mount
Modes	AM only
Squelch	Yes
Price	£175

WIN 108 dedicated VHF Airband receiver (*reproduced by kind permission of Lowe Electronics*)

A superb all-round performance which is particularly good at an airport, due to its light weight. It has 20 memories organised in two banks (A/B) of 10 memories. Both A0/B0 memory cells act as the *Priority* locations which are activated by a slide switch on the front of the receiver. When active, the radio checks the A0/B0 cells every 2 seconds for activity.

In Use

Accessing the various modes is simple and multiple key presses are kept to a minimum. The only time I had to look at the operating manual was to learn how to set the frequencies of the scan limits! I took one to Manchester and East Midlands airports. Having stored the relevant ATC frequencies in the receiver, I left it to get on with the job, which it did without any fuss or bother. Audio from the internal speaker was crisp and clear: the squelch very positive in operation. The receiver slipped easily into my jacket pocket, which just left the highly usable 'rubber duck' antenna poking out.

WIN 108 Summary

My comments earlier about using a handheld radio as a base receiver *do not* apply in this case: I attached it to my roof-mounted *Scanstick Antenna* and, even though I live in an area where just about every radio signal is an extremely strong one, the WIN 108 coped with extreme ease! From home I could hear (at good strength too!) Manchester Approach, Humberside and East Midlands Towers' and even Birmingham Radar! To say I was impressed is like saying locusts are rather fond of corn! I demonstrated it to a couple of guys I met at Manchester. The last I saw of them they were heading into the 'TAS' shop on the spectator terraces, to obtain a couple of their own!

During the writing of this book, I have borrowed numerous airband, Scanning and HF radio receivers for review purposes. Some were instantly disposable, others merely good. The WIN 108, without any reservations at all, is the best dedicated handheld airbands receiver I've tested, or indeed come across so far. It's also the one I keep at the side of my word processsor, happily monitoring the aircraft band as I write this. The only problem is going to be how to explain to Lowes why they can't have it back – at least, not yet!

SIGNAL R537S

Type	Handheld, crystal/VFO
Frequency range	118–136mHz via mechanical VFO or quartz crystal

Channel steps	—
Sensitivity	<1.8µV for 10dB S/N
Display	Crystal switch, VFO scale+index
Memories	None
Lock-out	No
Scan type	No scan
Scan speed	—
Search	No search
Power source	9 volts, from PP3 NiCad/dry battery, or external PSU
Aerial	Two, rubber helical & chrome whip, both 3.5mm jackplug mounted
Modes	AM only
Squelch	Yes
Price	£75

This receiver is favoured by free-fall parachutists: I ran over mine with my wheelchair, and it still works fine. From that, you'll no doubt gather that the SIGNAL R537S is tough. In fact, like all SIGNAL receivers, it is hand-made by an aviation enthusiast, with the casing formed out of mild steel. The 537S is a small radio, around the size of a cigarette packet, and very light. It weighs 300 grammes including aerial and battery, and is easily slipped into the pocket.

In Use

I've had one of these receivers for a number of years now, during which time it has performed faultlessly. Tuning is done either by the upright VFO wheel on the top plate, or by selecting either one of the maximum two crystals, via a switch. Being a dedicated (civil) airband receiver, the filtering, sensitivity and selectivity are just about perfect. The receiver is sensitive enough to hear what's going on, and selective enough to reject (often) extremely strong signals at an airport from items such as the ILS localiser, Glide Slope, Radar heads and other ATC transmissions.

SIGNAL R537S Summary

The R537S is a no-nonsense, no-compromise, virtually indestructible receiver, which covers all the basic requirements for listening to the civil (VHF) airband. It isn't a 'pretty' receiver to look at – none of the SIGNAL range are. Its beauty lies in its ease of use, and superlative performance on the airband. At first, setting the VFO is a bit fiddly, but you do quickly adapt. This is one of the cheapest airband receivers you'll come across, and SIGNAL receivers do maintain a high resale or trade-in value.

Sony AIR-7

Type	Handheld, synthesised
Frequency range	150–2194kHz (AM), 76–108mHz (FM), 108–136mHz (AIR), 144–174mHz (PSB)
Channel steps	5, 9, 25 or 50kHz
Sensitivity	FM=2μV, AIR=1.25μV, PSB=0.5μV
Display	Back-lit, digital LCD
Memories	40 (10 per band-range)
Lock-out	No – but see *Summary*
Scan type	Simple frequency, with delay or hold
Scan speed	5mHz in 7 seconds
Search	Simple memory search/program search, 10 memories per second
Power source	6 volts; from internal NiCad/dry batteries or external PSU
Aerial	Rubber helical, BNC mount
Modes	Wide-band FM, AM, Narrow-band FM
Squelch	Yes
Price	£150–£250

This is one of those receivers which doesn't fit neatly into my four categories, but as it's known as the 'AIR-7'; I've included it within the dedicated airband radios. The Air-7 has some powerful operating features but is simple to use. Whatever you want to do, whether simply tap in a frequency directly, or initiate a programmed memory search, it rarely takes more than a couple of key presses to get underway.

In Use

If ever Sony stopped dabbling in the specialist radio receiver market, and took the subject a whole lot more seriously, and realised that specialist receivers require *special IF filtering*, then they would indeed be a mighty force.

AIR-7 Summary

The AIR-7 has now been replaced by the AIR-8; but as yet I have no idea of the differences between the -7 and -8. The set has no lock-out, but neatly sidesteps the need for such a device by offering a *Program Memory Search*, where you dictate which memory locations will be searched and in what order. The normal memory search is a bit unique: memory locations run from 1 through 9 to 0. On a memory search, the search pattern is: 1, 4, 7, 0, 2, 5, 8, 3, 6, 9, 1.

If you want to search consecutive memory locations without setting up a program search, then remember to programme your memories in order; 1, 4, 7, etc. Do remember that connecting this receiver to an external antenna is not a good idea, the filter in the 455kHz IF simply can't cope with this amount of signal input.

ASA AIR PRO II

Type	Handheld, synthesised
Frequency range	520–1650kHz, 88–108mHz, 118–136mHz, 136–162.5mHz
Channel steps	9/10 and 25kHz
Sensitivity	AIR 4.1μV
Display	Back-lit, digital LCD
Memories	None
Lock-out	No
Scan type	—
Scan speed	—
Search	—
Power source	6 volt (× 4 dry batteries)
Aerial	Rubber helical & chromium whip
Modes	AM, FM
Squelch	Yes
Price	£60

This is a brave attempt to introduce an airbands receiver offering the basic, vital features, such as frequency synthesis and digital frequency display, but without any of the frills, like memories, scanning and searching etc. It's competing directly with the SIGNAL R537S, at around the same price, but the AIR PRO scores heavily with the direct digital frequency display.

At first sight, the sensitivity figure of the AIR PRO may appear off-putting, but you have to look at it in context. The radio is a handheld receiver, designed for use at outdoor locations, such as airports, airshows etc. At such events, the local signal levels are going to be very high, often around 1 volt! More than enough for even the deafest receiver! I'd be more inclined to worry about the AM filters and selectivity when at an airport, rather than the AIR PRO's sensitivity figure.

GROUP 2. SCANNING RECEIVERS

AOR 1000/Fairmate HP 100E Mk II

Type	Handheld, synthesised

Frequency range	8–600mHz (continuous), 805–1300mHz (continuous)
Channel steps	Programmable, from 5 to 995kHz in 5 or 12.5kHz steps
Sensitivity	8–550mHz & 805–1300mHz @ <0.5µV. 12dB SINAD. 25–550mHz @ <2µV. W.B.F.M. <3µV
Display	Back-lit, digital LCD
Memories	1000! Organised as ten banks of 100
Lock-out	Yes
Scan type	Simple frequency. Programmable – lower upper limit
Scan speed	40 channels per second
Search	Memory search, programmable memory search, special search bands
Power	4.8 internal NiCad battery pack
Aerial	Supplied dual-band rubber helical
Modes	AM, wide-band FM, narrow-band FM
Squelch	Yes
Price	£250

With such wide frequency coverage and so many memories, this receiver appears at face value to be enormously complicated to use. However, nothing could be further from the truth. The AOR 1000 – which, incidentally, also goes under many other names as well – has an astonishing range of features and facilities, covering just about any receive situation you can think of. And yet, it is perfectly possible simply to switch on this receiver and immediately access the frequency, or frequency range of your choice!

In Use

Frequency coverage of this receiver is organised as 10 Search Bands, which are accessible by the user via a simple key press. Band 1 covers the VHF civil airband, from 118 to 138mHz in 25kHz steps. Band 2 the military airband, from 225 to 400mHz in 50kHz steps. Band 6 the VHF Marine band, and Band 7 the UK Amateur Radio 2 metre VHF band. Of course, you're not stuck with these search bands; they can be re-programmed at any time by the user. For example, once you've gained some experience with the receiver, and in Scanning generally, you can re-programme the receiver to suit your own requirements.

AOR 1000 Summary

AOR have created a receiver with features which put certain base station scanners to shame! It has many advanced facilities, and yet remains simple to operate, the internal operating system software guides you through the correct key presses etc. The set does have an attenuator switch, so attaching an external aerial is a viable option.

Black Jaguar BJ200 Mk III

Type	Handheld, synthesised
Frequency range	26–30mHz, 50–88mHz, 115–178mHz, 210–280mHz, 360–520mHz
Channel steps	5, 10, 25kHz
Sensitivity	Generally, 1–1.5µV 10dB SINAD
Display	Back-lit, digital LCD
Memories	16
Lock-out	Yes
Scan type	User programmable (lower/upper limits) simple scan
Scan speed	10 channels per second
Search	Memory search @ 10 per second, hold or delay-then-continue
Power source	4.8 volts – internal NiCad pack, external 6 volts
Aerial	Rubber helical - space wound
Modes	User selectable AM & FM
Squelch	Yes
Price	Around £200 average

The single feature which endears the BJ200 to many military airband enthusiasts is this receiver's ability to let *you* select the operating mode! Many receivers choose the mode according to the frequency range selected and do not allow any over-ride. For example, some Scanners automatically switch to FM when tuning UHF ranges which is no use for listening to the UHF military airband on AM!

Black Jaguar BJ200 Mk III Summary

This is a particularly easy to use Scanner as it assigns just the one purpose to each of the keys, so there's no messing around with Second Function or Shift keys to access various options. Sensitivity and selectivity are both excellent, especially when used with its own rubber helical antenna. The only slight problem is that the minimum frequency step is 5kHz; some military airband frequencies are at 12.5kHz channel spacing. This means that you can't select the precise frequency of the service you're looking for, and have to settle for plus or minus 2.5kHz. In practice, the BJ200's IF filters are wide enough to allow for this slight frequency discrepancy.

AOR AR2002

Type	Base/mobile, synthesised
Frequency range	25–550mHz – continuous, 800–1300mHz – continuous
Channel steps	5, 12.5 25kHz
Sensitivity	NBFM 0.3μV, AM 0.5μV @ 10dB SINAD
Display	Back-lit, digital LCD
Memories	20
Lock-out	No (program search)
Scan type	Simple frequency, lower/upper limits
Scan speed	6 seconds per mHz
Search	Memory search, program memory search at 5 channels per second
Power source	External 12 volt
Aerial	Simple telescopic whip supplied (BNC)
Modes	AM, NBFM, WBAM
Squelch	Yes
Price	£480

The Scanner against which every other Scanner is judged! It provides complete coverage of the civil and military airbands, as well as all airport vehicle and ground movement frequencies. It's used by scientific, military and other governmental departments as a monitoring receiver, as well as thousands of other satisfied users.

AOR AR2002 Summary

The AR2002 is getting a little long in the tooth now, although it's still available. It has been superseded by the AOR AR3000 (see Review, later) and the new and very exciting AOR AR950UK, both of which actually improve on the AR2002's sensitivity/selectivity performance, and ease of use. It has an RS232 port for connection to a home computer, and Lowe Electronics of Matlock supply all of the interfacing hardware and software for connection to various microcomputers. Second-hand models do appear occasionally, and the relatively high price they fetch reflects exactly how good they are, and how much they're sought after.

GROUP 3. HIGH-FREQUENCY (SHORTWAVE) RADIO RECEIVERS

Lowe Electronics HF225

Type	Base, synthesised
Frequency range	30kHz to 30mHz continuous

Channel steps	8Hz, 50Hz, 125Hz/1.6kHz, 9kHz, 25kHz
Sensitivity	1.2μV to 0.3μV 10dB S/N
Display	Back-lit, digital LCD
Memories	30
Lock-out	No
Scan type	No scan
Scan speed	—
Search	—
Power source	External 12 volts from mains power (unit supplied)
Aerial	None supplied, binder posts for 600 ohm random wire antennas, SO239 socket for coaxial input
Modes	AM, synchronous AM (AMS)*, LSB, USB, CW, narrow-band FM*
Squelch	No
Price	£425

* Optional extra

A no-compromise, no-nonsense HF radio which is unique in that it's about the only HF receiver actually manufactured in the UK. Lowe Electronics of Matlock set out to design and build a receiver which offered the listener superb radio reception under even the most difficult of conditions, but without any of the bells, whistles and flashing light gadgets which usually add at least one nought to the final price. As if

Lowe Electronics HF225 HF communications receiver (*reproduced by kind permission of Lowe Electronics*)

that wasn't difficult enough, they then decided that it should have a final price which Mr and Mrs Average could afford without recourse to a second mortgage. They've succeeded brilliantly, and won themselves several international awards for this receiver into the bargain!

In Use

Having collected a review model from Lowes, I arrived home and connected it all together. Then something really strange happened. Having connected the HF225 to my nest of HF dipoles, I tapped in a Shanwick Oceanic frequency on the optional keypad and was then staggered to find the receiver absolutely bang-on frequency! Not nearly, nor almost; but absolutely spot-on. Once I'd entered the frequency I never had to touch the tuning again. In some thirty-odd years of using numerous HF receivers this has never happened to me before. I was impressed!

HF225 Summary

Like the SIGNAL range of receivers, the HF225 bears all the marks of being designed by a genuine enthusiast. The range of filters fitted as standard is most impressive, and make life much easier on the crowded HF bands. The tuning knob is a delight to use, covering 1.6kHz per revolution, which is about one single sideband station for each complete rotation of the knob. However, winding the knob a little faster changes the tuning rate to a much faster speed, ideal for getting around the bands quickly. There's not much I can say about the actual handling of the receiver; all the controls fell logically into place and made searching for various radio services so simple it almost takes all the fun out of it! Everything I wanted to hear I did, with less band noise, and interference from other, local stations than I've ever experienced on any other HF radio receiver. Yes, it really is that good!

There are various options for this receiver, one of which I would say is vital: the external keypad for direct entry of frequency. Of course, you can set the receiver to any frequency by use of the UP/DOWN mHz buttons and the tuning knob. The keypad allows you to tap in the frequency directly, giving access to any frequency in the receiver's range almost instantaneously – very handy when hopping from band to band.

I can only think of two things which would make this receiver absolutely unbeatable: an all-mode squelch control to allow remote tape recordings to be made, and a purpose designed VHF converter. Of course, any external VHF convertor can be used, but it would be so much nicer to have one especially designed to take advantage of the HF225's superb performance.

Howes DcRx Direct Conversion HF Receiver

Type	Base/mobile/portable, VFO
Frequency range	5.450mHz to 5.750mHz
Channel steps	VFO controlled
Sensitivity	Adequate
Display	Options (see *In Use*)
Memories	None
Lock-out	No
Scan type	—
Scan speed	—
Search	—
Power source	External 12 volts
Aerial	None supplied, SO239 socket for coaxial input
Modes	CW, SSB
Squelch	No
Price	Self-assembly kit @ £15.60, ready-built @ £21.50

This is the cheapest possible way to monitor the main High Frequency Aeronautical Mobile airband of 5.5–5.8mHz. You don't need to be an electronics whizzkid to build this little receiver as full step-by-step instructions are provided. However, you do need to know how to solder properly. If you're like me and can't even slice the top off your boiled egg without phoning the RAC, then you can buy the receiver module pre-built and tested. However, even when the finished receiver has been bought you still have to provide a suitable case to house it, with sockets for power and aerial.

In Use

There is an option to add a Light Emitting Diode (LED) direct digital frequency display, so an exact frequency can be tuned to. The same options apply to the frequency display kit as the receiver, you can build it yourself, or buy the completed module. The self-assembly kit costs £39.90, while the finished module will set you back £59.90.

Howes DcRx Summary

Mr Howes went to a lot of trouble to get a review receiver up to me, and having put it through its paces, I can't tell him how grateful I was! This little radio is an absolute snorter! Not only did I pick-up Shanwick Aeradio at enormous signal strength, using nothing but a random length (30 feet) of wire, but I could also hear the actual aircraft, often just entering the Gander Ocean Control Area, at enormous signal levels as well; all truly impressive.

Controls are minimal: there's a rotary volume control, a pre-selector (more of which in a moment) and the tuning control. That's it. I didn't have the Direct Digital Display module, which gives you a constant readout of frequency, so had to tune blind. Firstly the pre-selector control is turned until the background noise peaks, then the main tuning knob is twiddled until you find that OATCC frequency.

Kenwood R2000

Type	Base, synthesised
Frequency range	150kHz to 30mHz in 30, 1mHz bands, 118–174mHz with optional convertor
Channel steps	50Hz, 500Hz and 5kHz
Sensitivity	Less than 2µV 10dB S/N
Display	7-digit, fluorescent digital display to 100Hz res', memory number
Memories	10
Lock-out	No, programmable scan
Scan type	Set upper/lower scan limits
Scan speed	Unknown
Search	Individual memory search, programmable memory search
Power source	240 mains voltage, optional 12 volt supply
Aerials	None supplied, 500 ohm random wire binding posts. 50 ohm SO239 socket
Modes	AM, FM, SSB and CW
Squelch	Yes
Price	£600

This is Kenwood's lowest price HF receiver. Good-looking radios are

Kenwood R2000 HF communications receiver (*reproduced by kind permission of Lowe Electronics*)

a Kenwood trademark, and their on-air performance exactly matches their appearance. This receiver has a number of things going for it. Each of the memories acts as a separate VFO, allowing you to recall a memory and then tune away from the frequency. On other HF receivers, you usually have to cancel memory recall mode, re-select the VFO option and then tune the receiver. Although I may be accused of nit-picking, the R2000 has what I consider to be a very important feature – a forwards facing loudspeaker.

In Use

I set up the memories with various Oceanic Control frequencies, and initiated a programmed memory scan. The radio duly tramped up and down the memories, holding and then moving on as signals broke through the squelch threshold, stopping and starting the VOX mechanism of my tape recorder. I did find that on average the R2000 was a little noisier than the HF225, and this produced a lot of false starts of the tape recorder. However, like the HF225, I heard everything I searched for, and at good signal strength too.

I was particularly impressed with the performance of the 30-foot wire which I connected to the 500 ohm binder posts on the back of the receiver, without using an Aerial Tuning Unit (ATU). However, when using the ATU signals were obviously much louder with less background noise.

Kenwood R2000 Summary

Often, the airband radio listener has a problem in locating his/her 'listening post' in the home. The R2000 receiver wouldn't look out of place anywhere in a modern house. This receiver has two clocks, and a timer circuit which allows the radio to be automatically turned on and off at a preset time, enabling remote monitoring. There's a VHF converter module which fits internally, and covers the frequency range 118-174mHz, allowing you to listen to the VHF civil airband and various public utilities. Altogether, a well thought-out, very pretty and a highly usable receiver.

GROUP 4. TOTAL COVERAGE RECEIVERS

Any radio receiver purpose-designed for a particular activity is going to be better at that job than another radio designed to cover a range of activities. To expect a wide-range, multi-mode Scanning radio to outperform purpose-designed HF communications and dedicated airband receivers is foolish. Having said that, what's the advantage of having a multi-mode, wide frequency coverage Scanning receiver?

Buying such a receiver is always cheaper than buying the equivalent frequency coverage in separate radios. For example, receivers for the civil and military airbands and an HF communications receiver would add up to a huge amount. Buying just the one radio to cover all frequencies makes for a tidier desktop, removes the need for numerous coaxial cable runs and makes all of the receiver's various features available for all of its coverage.

Once you own such a receiver, you have the means to monitor all the HF airband frequencies, using the single sideband mode, all of the VHF civil airband, using the AM mode, and all of the military airband, using either AM or FM. As well as having access to all the UHF frequencies used by airport ground support vehicles, emergency services etc. Prices vary from around £400 up to several thousand.

There are several receivers which give continuous cover encompassing the HF, VHF and UHF airbands. But! They are limited to AM/FM, and have *no* single sideband reception mode. Therefore I have not included them here because without SSB they cannot resolve radio traffic on the HF airbands.

AOR AR3000

Type	Base/mobile, synthesised
Frequency range	100kHz to 2036mHz continuous
Channel steps	50Hz to 100kHz
Sensitivity	Average of 0.5μV
Display	Multi-purpose, back-lit digital LCD
Memories	400 (4 banks of 100)
Lock-out	Yes
Scan type	Simple frequency scan with delay, set lower/upper limits of scan
Scan speed	20 channels per second
Search	Memory search at 20 steps per second
Power source	External 12 volts (from supplied mains PSU)
Aerial	BNC fit whip, BNC socket
Modes	Wide-band FM, narrow-band FM, AM, LSB, USB, CW
Squelch	Yes
Price	£765

It really is hard to believe that this tiny receiver can do the things it does. A lot of thought has obviously gone into the operating system software, and although virtually all keys have a dual purpose, using the radio is straightforward.

In Use

The AR3000's memories can store frequency, attenuator control setting and mode. I programmed the memories with a mixture of VHF, UHF and SSB, HF frequencies, and let the machine do its stuff. The first thing you notice is the speed with which it searches the memories – very fast. I compared its performance at certain frequencies with dedicated receivers. For example, on the VHF civil airband I connected my roof-mounted scanning antenna to my SIGNAL R532 and the AR3000 receivers via a coaxial switch. Flicking between the two radios, I couldn't detect any differences at all, which is praise for the AR3000 as I consider the R532 to be the best dedicated mobile civil airband receiver ever made.

On the HF aeronautical airbands, I used the same coaxial switch to my nest of dipoles, and switched between the AR3000 and the Lowes HF225. The HF225 was generally much quieter overall, producing radio signals which were a pleasure to hear. The AR3000, although producing a noisier background, still heard everything the HF225 did, which is after all, the name of the game.

AOR AR3000 Summary

Just like its stablemates, the AR3000 adds further to the AOR company's excellent reputation as manufacturers of fine Scanning receivers. VHF and UHF airband performance was superb, exceeding that of the AR2002: the HF performance was good too. This receiver has an RS232 port to allow direct connection to a home computer. Aerials may be a problem as it's virtually impossible to obtain an antenna to cover this wide frequency range, so you'll need aerials for HF and discones etc. for VHF/UHF.

Sony ICF PRO-80

Type	Handheld, synthesised
Frequency range	150kHz to 216mHz continuous
Channel steps	3, 5, (9)/10 & 50kHz + fine-tune
Sensitivity	Average of 1.5µV 10dB S/N
Display	Multi-purpose, back-lit digital LCD
Memories	40
Lock-out	No, program search
Scan type	Simple frequency, hold/delay, priority scan

Scan speed	Not known
Search	Memory search, program search
Power source	Internal 6 volts (batteries)
Aerial	Plastic whip (special, Sony fit)
Modes	Wide/narrow-band AM, wide/narrow-band FM, USB, LSB, CW
Squelch	Yes
Price	£350

Stablemate to the Sony AIR-7, the PRO-80 covers 150kHz to 108mHz in its basic form. Adding the (supplied) FRG80 convertor – a box which connects between the receiver's antenna and the aerial socket, extends the frequency range up to the maximum 216mHz.

In Use

This receiver provides complete coverage of the HF, and VHF airbands but only partial coverage of the UHF, military airband. It works well with its supplied aerial, but can be overloaded when connected to a large, external antenna array. With so many features and facilities, the top-plate of the receiver is a bit crowded.

Sony ICF PRO-80 Summary

A useful, 'take-anywhere' receiver which performs well on its own aerial. There is a 'Fine-Tune' control to allow exact netting to an SSB signal. Supplied accessories include the FRG80 frequency convertor, a soft carry case and shoulder belt plus various frequency guide-type booklets.

Yaesu FRG 9600 (RAYCOM)*

Type	Base, synthesised
Frequency range	200kHz to 950mHz (RAYCOM)*
Channel steps	100Hz, 1.5, 10, 12.5, 25 & 100kHz
Sensitivity	Average 1μV
Display	Fluorescent, digital
Memories	100
Lock-out	Yes
Scan type	Simple frequency, set upper/lower scan limits, hold & delay
Scan speed	Unknown
Search	Memory search, program search
Power source	External, 12 volts

Aerial	Supplied .6 metre whip, SO239 socket
Modes	Wide/narrow-band AM, wide/narrow-band FM, USB, LSB, CW
Squelch	Yes
Price	£650 (RAYCOM)*

* *Note* In its basic form, this receiver only covers the frequency range 60 to 905mHz. However, Raycom Communications System Limited (address in the Appendices) provide a customising service, fitting various modifications to the basic FRG9600 which extends the frequency downwards to 200kHz, and upwards to 950mHz. It is possible to buy this receiver new and guaranteed from Raycom with the modifications already made; or you may have an un-modified FRG9600 converted by them for a fee.

In Use

This popular, Raycom modified scanning receiver provides complete coverage of the HF, VHF and military UHF airbands, as well as airport ground vehicle UHF frequencies. I haven't been able to obtain a modified version for reviewing, but I do have a friend who owns one. From what he tells me, this receiver is equally happy in a car as it is in the home. The scan and search features are simple to operate, and quite powerful in use.

Yaesu, the manufacturers of this receiver, also provide a couple of convertors: the FC965DX extends the frequency range to encompass 150kHz to 30mHz, while the FC1300 extends the top-end frequency coverage to 800-1300mHz. Both of the Yaesu convertors connect externally though.

Yaesu FRG 9600 Summary

The price of the basic FRG 9600 receiver is £520. A Raycom modified version – and incidentally, Raycom has earned an excellent world-wide reputation for its FRG9600 conversion, costs £650 which is cheaper than buying the basic receiver plus the two Yaesu external convertors. The modified version has all the work done internally, presenting a clean radio with no external boxes or wires, which is important to some people.

AIRBAND RADIO RECEIVERS: A FINAL SUMMARY

Whatever type of receiver you ultimately decide upon, remember; use it within its design limits. *Any* receiver is only as good as the aerial it is connected to. It's a nonsense to spend several hundred pounds on the receiver only to begrudge spending a few pounds on a decent antenna system.

My Personal Selection

Of all the receivers reviewed, bought or borrowed from friends – which is quite a lot, believe me – some were brilliant, others a joke, which would be funny if it wasn't for their cost. My personal favourites are:

The WIN 108 handheld, dedicated civil airband receiver, which not only performed superbly well at various airports, but is also the nearest you'll get to one receiver to cover base, portable and mobile use. It retained its impeccable peformance even when connected to a large, external aerial, and is the best receiver of its type I've ever tested.

The HF225 short wave band receiver, for its sheer performance, which nearly always beat the pants off receivers costing two to three times more!

The SIGNAL 535S for being designed and built by an airband enthusiast for other airband radio listeners, and for its superb performance on both the civil and military airbands, while still retaining its ease of use.

Howes DcRx short wave airbands receiver kit, for being the cheapest possible alternative to a full-blown HF communications receiver.

And last but by no means least, the tiny but powerful AOR AR950UK Base/Mobile Scanner, for offering a brilliant receiver at a very reasonable price.

AIRBAND RADIO AERIALS – VHF/UHF

The antenna is the single, most important link in the whole airband listening chain. There is absolutely no point whatever in spending £300 to £800 on a receiver only to stuff a coat hanger in the antenna socket. You would be amazed by the number of people who are willing to spend this kind of money on a receiver and then begrudge spending another £25 for a decent aerial. A good antenna and earth system can make a poor receiver sound good: a bad aerial/earth combination makes even a fantastic receiver sound terrible.

External Antennas. Why Bother?

The average airband radio listener spends more time listening from home than at an airport. An external antenna at your home location can really open up the listening potential of your receiver, allowing you to hear other aviation-based services which you may have never heard before. Services such as En-route, as well as airport ATC, various Company transmissions, VOLMET stations, Oceanic clearances etc. The cost of external antennas varies greatly, from almost nothing by making your own (it really is very simple) to around a £100 for a multi-frequency Log-Periodic beam array. But before explaining the various types of external airband aerials, let's look at some common problems – maybe you'll recognise yourself?

The Problems

Listener 'A' lives in a heavily built-up area of a city, surrounded by tall buildings made from lots of reinforced steel-cored concrete. Her local council will allow external radio and TV aerials, as long as they look reasonable (the definition of reasonable lies with them!). There is an airport in her city, around 20 miles or so from where she lives, but she can't hear any R/T traffic, except an occasional call from an aircraft. Listener 'A' wants to hear the airport, and En-route ATC radio messages, because at the moment she's quite disappointed with her new VHF airband receiver.

Listener 'B' resides just outside a fairly large market town. He lives on the top of a small hill around 100 metres above sea level. His immediate surroundings are fairly flat, wooded countryside, sloping gently away on all sides. There are many small airfields within 25 miles' radius, and he has three large regional airports, and Manchester International all within an approximate 50 mile radius. He can hear quite a lot of airways and military radio traffic, but can only just detect Air Traffic Control (ATC) at the airports, even though he can quite clearly receive the aeroplanes responding to them. Listener 'B' wants to listen to the airport ATC, and extend the coverage of his Scanning receiver to include RAF bases in Lincolnshire, around 50 miles to the east of him.

Listener 'C' lives on the top of a very high hill in Derbyshire. She can hear lots of airband radio traffic from all over the place, including many airports. Occasionally, when she's listening to a certain frequency, another station suddenly comes 'over the top' of the one she's listening to, and completely spoils her fun. She knows that this isn't a selectivity problem because she's using a top-of-the-range dedicated airbands receiver. Listener 'C' wants to listen to her favourite stations without other airband radio traffic wiping them out.

Listener 'D'. He is physically disabled and doesn't get out much because of illness. He lives in a second floor flat within a high-rise tower block. External aerials are not allowed under any circumstances. Listener 'D' is a potential plane spotter and would very much like to listen to all the available airbands. Knowing the aerial situation, he's doubtful about what he could hear from home. He once borrowed a friend's VHF airband receiver, but it wasn't a very good one, and he heard almost nothing. And then one day he bought a book called *The Aviation Euthusiast's Handbook*, which completely changed his life!

Finally, Listener 'E' is a sales representative who spends a great deal of time in her car, travelling around the country from appointment to meeting. She's a keen plane spotter with a Scanning receiver on the passenger seat, working off its own internal whip aerial. She doesn't hear a lot of airband messages, but can get the odd signal, especially when passing near an RAF aerodrome or civil airport. Listener E is vaguely aware that there are specialised shops where purpose-built, mobile airband antennas can be bought, but she doesn't know where and, even if she did she wouldn't really know what to ask for.

ANTENNA BACKGROUND INFORMATION

The Resonant Aerial

Before I move on to suggesting solutions for Listeners A-E, I first want to introduce you to the concept of the 'resonant aerial'. Resonance is the antenna's ability to vibrate at a specific frequency, in much the same way that an opera singer can shatter a champagne glass by singing a note of the same natural frequency as the glass. Any piece of wire pushed up into the air will collect radio waves of all frequencies, indis-criminately – accepting wheat as well as chaff, no matter that you only want the wheat!

However, a resonant aerial will still collect radio waves of all frequencies, but will respond best to those which match its own, natural frequency, making them appear to be much 'louder' in the receiver's speaker, and will help reduce those radio signals outside the resonance range of the antenna. This is why such aerials are only good for the frequency for which they are designed.

Resonance is dictated by the physical length of the aerial, which has to be cut to a specific size for resonance at a required frequency. There are formulae to work this out for you, see Diagram 3. So, the ideal to aim for is an aerial which is resonant at the frequency which is to be listened to. For listening to the VHF airband, you require an aerial which is resonant between 118–137mHz. The most famous resonant aerials are: the Half-Wave Dipole, and the Quarter-Wave Ground Plane.

Polarized Antennas

Apart from antenna resonance, you also have to bear in mind the polarization of the transmitted radio signal. Radio waves are either

DIAGRAM 3. RESONANT AERIALS.

The Half-Wave Dipole

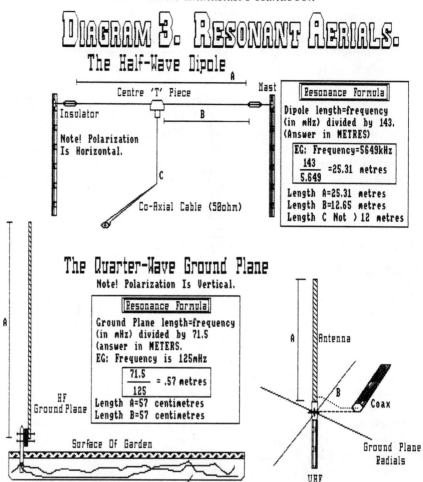

Centre 'T' Piece

Mast

Insulator

B

Note! Polarization
Is Horizontal.

C

Co-Axial Cable (50ohm)

Resonance Formula

Dipole length=frequency
(in mHz) divided by 143.
(Answer in METRES)

EG: Frequency=5649kHz

$$\frac{143}{5.649} = 25.31 \text{ metres}$$

Length A=25.31 metres
Length B=12.65 metres
Length C Not ⟩ 12 metres

The Quarter-Wave Ground Plane

Note! Polarization Is Vertical.

Resonance Formula

Ground Plane length=frequency
(in mHz) divided by 71.5
(answer in METERS.
EG: Frequency is 125mHz

$$\frac{71.5}{125} = .57 \text{ metres}$$

Length A=57 centimetres
Length B=57 centimetres

A

HF
Ground Plane

Surface Of Garden

Ground Plane Radials (Buried).

B

Antenna

A

B

Coax

Ground Plane
Radials

VHF
Ground Plane

vertically, or horizontally polarized. To receive the best possible signal into your airband receiver, your aerial should be resonant at the working frequency, and erected in the correct polarization plane i.e. vertical for a vertically transmitted radio wave, and horizontal for a horizontally emitted signal. All VHF airband radio signals are Vertically Polarized.

Having your antenna on the wrong polarization, eg. horizontal when receiving a vertically polarized signal, incurs a penalty of lost signal, often as much as half. Imagine, the station you're listening to could be twice as loud if only the polarization of your aerial matched the transmitter's!

MAKING A DIPOLE AERIAL.

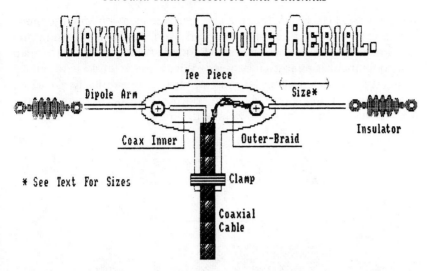

Tee Piece

Dipole Arm

Size*

Coax Inner

Outer-Braid

Insulator

* See Text For Sizes

Clamp

Coaxial
Cable

Feeders

And then there's the feeder to consider too! Perhaps you're just beginning to realise why I get a little annoyed with various authors who advocate slinging a random length of trawler-towing steel hawser out of the bedroom window, to use as an 'all bands wonder-twig'! The feeder is the part of the aerial system which collects the induced radio signal from the aerial, and delivers it to the receiver. It is usually (but by no means always) made from a co-axial cable (coax) just like your TV feeder cable.

Next to the actual aerial itself, the feeder system is the next most crucial element. Precious signal, painstakingly acquired by your antenna, can be, and is, lost within the coaxial cable. The longer the feeder, then the more signal you will lose. If you really cannot position your receiver close to the mast/aerial combination, then do not use the 'thin', CB type of coax known as UR43. Switch to the much thicker (and of course, more expensive!) UR67 coax, where signal losses within are much less than with thinner cables.

Any feeders longer than around 40 feet should *not* be of UR43 coaxial cable. Also beware of the coaxial cable's impedance. Most modern receivers need a coax cable with 50 ohms impedance: using 75 ohm TV coax is not a cheap alternative; and again will result in potential received signal unnecessarily lost in the impedance mismatch.

The Solutions

Listener A's predicament is very common. A new airband receiver is bought, rushed home, the whole family assembled, the radio switched on. And; NOTHING! Within the city there are many buildings to block out airband radio transmissions, and with Listener A using the receiver's own aerial because she hasn't yet an external one, then disappointment is almost guaranteed. What she has to do is to put up some type of external aerial system, such as a vertically polarized dipole, or a ground plane, both of which should be resonant on the VHF airband. Diagram 4 shows how to do this.

Listener B receives (in his opinion) very good signals from the TV aerial he uses as an antenna on his Scanner receiver, but he wants to listen to military airband signals a good distance away, as well as the local airport. Now, a Scanning receiver is very different to a VHF-only airband receiver because the Scanner covers a range of different frequency bands, compared to the VHF set's single band. Therefore, resonance is going to be a problem. Military airband radio takes place on the UHF band, civil on the VHF. It is difficult to make *one* antenna resonant over a wide frequency range, such as VHF AND UHF, but it can be done.

Listener B's logical answer is to erect separate (resonant) antennas for each frequency band covered by his Scanner. The problem being the eventual amount of metal in the air, and the expense of multiple feeder runs. In radio, as the frequency gets higher, then aerial size becomes smaller and smaller. For example, a resonant ground plane antenna for a frequency of 7000kHz is some 32 feet tall, while the same aerial cut for resonance at 125mHz is only 21 inches! There are various designs of antenna which offer resonance over a fairly wide frequency range, such as the Discone and the Multi-Band Ground Plane. Both work in much the same way.

So instead of going to all the bother of erecting separate aerials for each band covered by his Scanner, Listener B now only needs to put up a discone antenna, which covers the desired frequency range, and he's got what he wanted; a good, external aerial which will allow him to receive much better signals from the local airport and the distant RAF bases. Because the discone is resonant on the civil airband *and* the UHF military airband, as well as other frequencies, Listener B has the ideal antenna for his Scanner, and only the one feeder too!. Or has he?

Discone wide-band Scanning aerial

One little known fact about discone antennas, which are, by the way, very popular in the Scanning world, is their polarization pattern – which is, for all intents and purposes, horizontal! As you now know, there's a heavy penalty to pay for being on the wrong polarization in terms of lost signal.

Listener B may be much better suited by acquiring a Multi-Band Ground Plane, which is most definitely vertically polarized! You will find that most of the radio signals people equipped with Scanning receivers like to listen to are vertically polarized; so do bear this in mind when searching for an external aerial for your Scanner.

Listener C has the opposite problem to both Listeners A and B. She can hear far too much! Frequency sharing on the VHF airband (and others too!) is quite common. Stations sharing the same frequencies are widely separated geographically, so that mutual interference is kept to a minimum. Unfortunately for Listener C, she's slap-bang in the middle of this geographical separation zone, and is receiving two services on the same frequency. She has two basic choices: either reduce the effectiveness of her present antenna system, so that it picks up less signal, or replace it altogether with a different type of aerial.

Reducing the effectiveness of the existing aerial isn't easy, nor is it a good idea either. If you make the antenna 'deaf' then it will be 'deaf' for *all* signals, the wanted as well as the unwanted ones. A better option would be replacement. Listener C can try exchanging her external ground plane antenna system for some form of directional *beam* aerial.

Armed with a directional beam antenna and rotator, Listener C can then point it towards various ATC services, while avoiding others. As beam antennas collect most signal from the front, and very little from the back, this is one way of avoiding interference.

Listener D's case does, on the face of it, look hopeless. No way! For such people who cannot erect external aerials, there's much that can be done, and using the most surprising everyday materials too. For example, a Full-Wave VHF Loop aerial can be made from aluminium 'burglar alarm' tape and run around the inside of a suitably facing window frame. But for those people like me who are a complete klutz with their hands, there's *Active Antennas*.

Active Aerials

An active aerial usually comprises a 'short' whip, or some other form of signal gathering metal, like wire dipole arms, and a box of electronics which amplifies the radio signals gathered by the short whip. Any amplification of incoming radio signals has to be done with extreme caution. Boosting the signal is very easy, but unless the active aerial has special safeguards (price is an excellent guide) it will also amplify all of the band noise as well. Poorly designed active antennas can and will introduce your receiver to selectivity troubles; replacing one set of problems with a whole lot of new ones, leaving you worse off than before you started – and obviously that much poorer in the pocket too!

For the flat dweller, or anyone else not allowed external aerials, the active antenna is a boon. It can sit quite comfortably on a window ledge, or balcony, and if well designed, pull in signals which can leave you amazed why others prefer the hassle of huge, outdoor antenna 'farms'. Active aerials can now be had to cover the complete short wave airbands, from 2–28mHz, and for VHF/UHF airbands as well.

Listener D need only acquire active aerials for the appropriate bands he wants to listen to, and he's in business. They are relatively inexpensive, take up little or no space, and can be carried out onto a balcony, or fastened to a window ledge and at the end of the day, removed and stored. Much simpler than applying for planning permission to erect a flag pole, drilling out the centre and filling the middle of the pole with aerial wire!

Mobile Antennas

Listener E has a wide variety of choice for her predicament – and that's often the problem. With so many antennas to choose from, which one is going to be the right one?

Mobile antennas usually follow the form of the Multi-Band Ground Plane, except that the actual ground-plane radials are removed, the car's metal roof replacing their function. I use a Multi-Band Ground Plane of the 'radome' type, ie. the various quarter wave elements are contained inside a white glass fibre shell. Although I don't own a Scanner, this type of aerial is designed for one.

Other mobile aerials take the form of a single steel element with various coil mechanisms dotted along their length, again offering multi-frequency operation. You can, of course, buy single band quarter-wave ground plane antennas, for either VHF or UHF; but then, you can just as easily make one for yourself!

Mobile antennas are attached to the car by either the 'Gutter Mount' (a variation of which is the 'Boot-Lip Mount') or by 'Mag-Mount', which is a magnetic disc on top of which is a socket to accept the aerial. For permanent location of whatever type of aerial you choose the gutter mount has much to recommend it. It is semi-permanent, very rigid and relatively inexpensive. As its name suggests, it is clamped to the car's gutter channel with two allen bolts. Fine if your car has a gutter – mine doesn't. The actual aerial part is designed to be removed while leaving the mount in-situ.

The mag-mount is designed for those people who do not want a permanent connection to the car or who have a vehicle without gutters. When needed it is slapped onto the roof, making sure that it's seated firmly, the antenna attached, coax plugged-in, and you're away. Removing it after use only takes a minute.

HF Antennas

As previously stated, a rise in frequency produces a shortening of the actual aerial. This of course works equally well in reverse; and the first thing you'll have to get used to on the High Frequency airbands is the huge (compared to V/UHF) size of the antennas! There are various ways of compacting HF aerials, trading off performance against array size. So, starting with the biggest arrays first, I'll scale down later.

You've already met the resonant Half-Wave Dipole; using the formula in Diagram 3, work out the size of dipole needed for the 5.5mHz HF airband. Big isn't it? When it comes to fitting such an aerial into your back garden, bear this in mind. A) it doesn't have to be laid

Diagram 5. Small Gardens

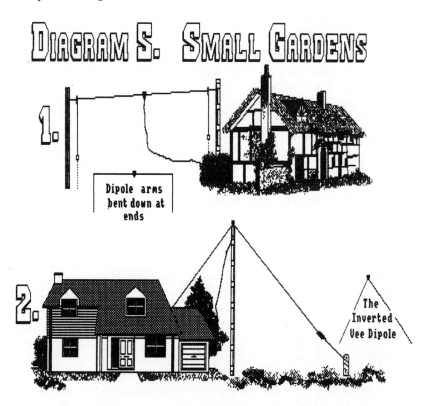

1. Dipole arms bent down at ends

2. The Inverted Vee Dipole

Small Gardens, Making The Dipole Fit

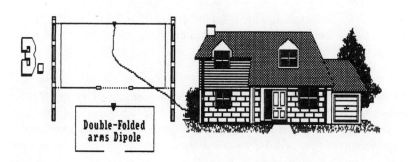

3. Double-Folded arms Dipole

out like a washing line, eg. straight as an arrow, from end to end. And B) you may be limited for space lengthways and breadthways, but not many gardens are limited in space *vertically*! Diagram 5 illustrates various ways of shoe-horning this 5.5mHz dipole array into an average garden.

Still taking advantage of the height possibilities in the back garden, from the formula supplied in Diagram 3, work out the size for a Quarter-Wave Ground Plane – but do remember, the actual ground plane itself is a vital part of the system, and should not be 'bodged'. Both of these very simple and inexpensive 'full-sized' 5.5mHz arrays will perform brilliantly; you'll not miss a thing when listening to the 5.5mHz airband with either of these aerials.

Buy Or Build?

HF dipoles and ground planes are simple to build and cost virtually nothing. You can, however, buy multi-band dipole arrays, and multi-band, trapped ground planes – but they're almost universally made to work on frequencies used by radio amateurs, and as such won't be resonant on the frequencies you'll need; although there are ways to induce resonance.

The Long Wire

The Long Wire holds the current record for being the most misunderstood aerial of all time. Its name refers to wavelength and not the actual size of the piece of wire itself. It is 'long' in terms of the frequency on which it is to be used. For example, a 132-foot wire used on a frequency of 28mHz is a true long wire, because the actual length of the wire is much longer than the wavelength of 28mHz which is approximately 10 metres. However, the same length of wire used on a frequency of 2mHz is a 'short' wire, because the length is shorter than the wavelength.

The Aerial Tuning Unit (ATU)

Long wires are *not* resonant. They have resonance thrust upon them in the shape of an Aerial Tuning Unit (ATU). The ATU is an electro-mechanical device which uses coils of wire and variable capacitors to adjust the wire's resonance at various frequencies. Again, fundamental aerial erection rules apply: as much wire as you can, as high as you can, but this time you'll need that ATU as well.

When running out your long wire, keep it well clear of TV aerials, which radiate an electronic hash from the television set's timebase, and surrounding buildings. Don't simply tack one end onto a convenient tree. Yours wouldn't be the first chimney pot which was wrenched off the roof by the tree-end of the wire blowing around in a gale!

Earth Connection

A long wire (much like other HF aerial systems) needs a good earth connection. The house mains earth is *not* suitable. All the electrical devices in your home which require earthing will be connected to this mains earth. In practice this means that any interference, such as that from a central heating thermostat (very common problem), or the compressor of an old fridge, will be shared around the house, passing along the electrical wiring. All that 'noise' will be carried straight into your receiver if you connect it to the house earth. Therefore, you'll have to run out your own, separate earthing line for your receiver(s) (see Diagram 6).

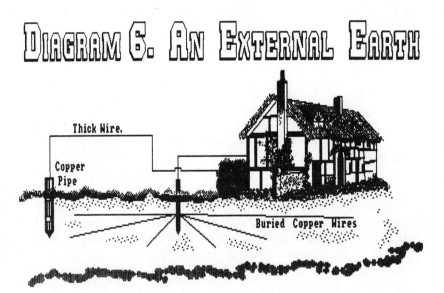

Diagram 6. An External Earth

Thick Wire.

Copper Pipe

Buried Copper Wires

In use, a good electrical earth is made by driving a copper, or metal spike deep into the ground, and connecting it to the 'EARTH' terminal on the ATU with a thick cable. The long wire is brought into the operating room (where you do your listening) and connected to the 'ANT' terminal on the ATU. The receiver is tuned to the wanted frequency, the equivalent range set on the ATU, and then the 'TUNING' controls (of the ATU) are tweaked for the loudest signal in the receiver.

Counterpoise Earth

If you live in high-rise flats you won't have access to a garden, and so can't make your own earthing arrangements; at least, on the face of it. Another type of earthing arrangement which works very well for long wire antennas is the Counterpoise Earth. What you do is to cut another length of wire, which has to be the same length as your long wire. Where you put it isn't critical. I tuck mine under the carpet of the room where my receivers are, but you could just as easily run it around the skirting board. Connect the end of this wire to the EARTH terminal of the ATU. As you tune the Aerial Tuning Unit you bring the long wire into resonance *and* the counterpoise earth at the same time.

Many HF airband listeners simply 'hang up' a long wire, and shove the end straight into the receiver, not bothering with an ATU, or even any earthing. All I can say about this is; borrow an ATU and try it. *You will not believe the difference it makes!* Next add an earth, either direct or counterpoise, and watch the band noise vanish as well.

Summary

All of the aerial systems I've discussed will make a tremendous difference to airband listening from your home – where almost 90% of listening takes place. I've concentrated mainly on antennas which you can construct, with little or no previous skill or experience necessary. Aerial experimenting is tremendous fun, and in no time at all you'll be putting up 'designer' arrays of your own! Here is a brief summary of all aerials discussed.

Ground Plane

This simple antenna works very well indeed. It consists of two main parts: the centre element which connects to the feeder coax inner, and the three or four ground plane radials which connect to the coax outer braiding. Note that the centre element *must be* insulated from the ground plane radials. A variation of the ground plane is the 'Unipole' Ground Plane. Most specialist airband shops, and airband receiver suppliers stock various forms of the ground plane, and they are relatviely inexpensive as well.

Dipole

The most versatile of all aerials. It consists of two arms which connect to either a home-made 'T' piece, or a commercial dipole centrepiece. The inner/outer of the feeder coax connect to either arm of the 'T' centrepiece. Maximum signal is picked up when the dipole is at right angles to the transmitter, minimum signal is picked up off the dipole ends, so be careful where you put it. If your wanted signal is coming from an airport due east of you, then align your dipole north/south.

Modern receivers need a coaxial feeder cable impedance of 50 ohms, so ensure that you do actually use 50 ohm coax for the dipole feeder. Further, on the back of such receivers, there are wire terminal posts, for an aerial wire. They are usually marked something like ANT 500 Ohms; or sometimes, 600 Ohm Wire. These are designed for connection to a random length of wire, and earth.

At the side of these terminal posts there is an SO239 socket, which accepts type PL259 coaxial plugs. The impedance of this socket is 50 ohm. Ensure that the coax dipole feeder is properly terminated with a PL259 plug *and* that you screw this plug into the SO239 socket. There's absolutely no point at all in leaving off the PL259 plug from the coax feeder, separating the inner/outer wires and fastening them to the 500 ohm terminal posts.

The Discone

The Discone looks for all the world like a hedgehog laid on its back and impaled on a stick. It achieves resonance over a wide frequency range by having one pair of dipole elements for each frequency band covered. Typical coverage of a discone is something like: 70–700mHz. But do beware of totally outrageous statements for 'suspect' discones, such as the following:

'Covers 1 Hertz right up to 20,000 GigaHertz!'

Such an aerial already exists – most people call them garden fences! Discones do come in various frequency ranges, such as the above, and 100–900mHz, or 200–1296mHz. The idea is that you choose the frequency range you're most interested in. Erecting the discone is the same for any antenna: as high as you can, as clear from obstructions as you can get it. Not forgetting to use UR67 coaxial cable if the run from the aerial to the receiver is greater than around 40 feet.

But remember what I said earlier about the discone; it is a horizontally polarized antenna, and as you know there's a heavy penalty in terms of lost signal for being on the wrong polarization.

Multi-Band Ground Plane

This is basically the Quarter-Wave Ground Plane with multiple quarter-wave centre elements cut for the various frequency ranges covered. They are sometimes encapsulated within fibre glass or plastic. Other types use a single centre element with 'loading coils' along the length. They can be obtained in both 'Base Station' and 'Mobile' configurations. Buy from the specialist airband shops or the airband radio suppliers.

Beams

Individual frequency band beams, such as VHF civil, and UHF military airbands may be bought from the usual sources. They usually take the form of a three or four element 'Yagi' design. The Log Periodic beam is deservedly popular. Again, like the true discone, it has a pair of dipole elements for each frequency band covered. The lowest frequency, longest elements are fixed at the back of the log periodic, and the highest frequency, smallest elements are at the front. This type of beam is capable of very wide frequency coverage, and high gain.

BUT! Remember this! If you buy a beam, whether a Yagi-type or a log periodic, then you'll also have to purchase a 'Rotator' to enable you to point the beam in various directions. Without the rotator your beam will be fixed, pointing in one direction permanently. (See Accessories.)

ACCESSORIES

Rotators

As previously stated, if you're going to use some form of beam antenna then you'll have to get yourself a rotator too. The rotator is simply an electric motor onto which the aerial is bolted. A control box turns power on and off to the motor, and drives the beam around to the wanted direction. Costs vary, but by judicious shopping around, you should be able to get something new for around £60.

Pre-Amplifiers

Assuming that you've got an external aerial, fitted with UR67 feeder, and a first-class airbands receiver – and it's still not enough! You could try a pre-amp. These devices boost received signal strength, as well as any band noise. The best type to buy is the Masthead GasFet. This is a box which you fit on top of the pole supporting the aerial, so that the pre-amp sits just underneath the antenna.

The coax from the antenna goes into the masthead pre-amp box, where the electronics inside boost the signal and send it down the feeder to the receiver. Of course the masthead pre-amp needs power, and this is usually delivered to the control box via the coax feeder, which saves you running extra cables up the mast to the antenna. GasFet is a type of 'transistor' device in the box which does the amplifying, and represents 'state-of-the-art' (the best you can get). Very little boosting of the signal is necessary at VHF/UHF frequencies, and even less is required for the HF airbands.

Another type of pre-amp is the sort which fastens either directly between the antenna and the receiver on a handheld, or fits inside the casing of a base station receiver. Either way, the concept is the same. Radio signals are carried from the aerial down into the pre-amp. There they are boosted and then fed into the receiver.

A third type of pre-amp, and by far the best type for listening on the HF airbands, is the Pre-Selector, which in effect adds another (tuned) RF stage at the front end (where the signals enter) of the receiver. Basically, the pre-selector has a tuning arrangement and a low-level amplifier. The tuned circuits in the pre-selector help the amplifier part to reject unwanted radio signals, while boosting those signals that are wanted. Unfortunately, they're quite rare now.

Finally

There is a great deal of misinformation around concerning aerials, whether for VHF, UHF or HF. I have tried to present a technical subject in a non-technical way, concentrating entirely on basic principles and aerial projects a raw beginner can tackle with confidence. The antennas discussed do not represent cutting edge technology, however, they are all tried and proven designs which are very cheap to make and work very well. Don't be afraid to experiment with your own designs; you cannot harm your receiver by trying different antenna systems, and you may well come up with an entirely new design.

Part 2

Airport Operations and UK Guide

Larger airports are often like small towns; with their own police force, medical and fire services, their own transport system, shops, banks, kitchens and sometimes even their own power stations. Within this small town many people work, doing a variety of jobs from mopping floors, to repairing the engines of a jetliner.

In the UK, airport ownership is roughly in three categories. 1) Local authorities, or often a group of such authorities as at East Midlands Airport, where Nottinghamshire, Derbyshire and Leicestershire are the controlling shareholders. 2) Private companies, such as London City Airport. 3) The British Airports Authority (BAA).

Control Tower and ATCC sub-centre, Manchester Airport

BAA and CAA

The BAA own and run the following airports: Heathrow, Gatwick, Stansted, Aberdeen, Edinburgh, Glasgow and Prestwick, some of the busiest terminals in the world. The United Nations organisation, International Civil Aviation Organisation (ICAO), regulates aviation throughout the world, arranging various standards so that aircraft may fly safely from country to country, without worrying about the rules being changed half-way across the ocean! ICAO regulations are administered in this country by the Civil Aviation Authority (CAA) which effectively runs aviation in the United Kingdom. The CAA regulates airports, issuing licences, and lays down various standards for commercial pilots and the equipment an airport must have before handling a particular aircraft type.

Airports are run as money-making businesses by the owners, whether BAA, municipal or private. They make their money in the following ways. Direct charges to airline companies for aircraft landings, take-offs and use of airport facilities, such as air traffic control, check-in staff, aircraft maintenance and fuel, baggage handling etc. more of which later.

For example, a fully laden Boeing 747 from New York, carrying the maximum number of passengers, landing at Heathrow during peak times (early morning/afternoon) will be charged something like £6,500, which is made up from passenger charges, ATC and Navigation charges, and the actual landing itself. And that doesn't include use of any apron services. Then there's a parking fee of around £300 per hour too!

Surprisingly, landing/take-off fees only provide around 50% of an airport's revenue. The rest comes from services provided by the airport authority, such as apron and maintenance facilities, rent from the various airport franchises, such as shops, cafeterias, restaurants, bars etc. Advertising, car parking and duty free shops also provide a large slice of the airport's total income too; although the actual services themselves may be farmed out to private enterprise. For example, the car parking franchise is delegated to National Car Parks at many airports. NCP then pay the airport a fee for being allowed to do so.

The Runway

Aircraft mostly land and take-off into the wind; therefore the runway or runways have to be aligned along the direction of the prevailing wind, which for this country, is mostly from the west. Diagram 7 shows a fairly typical runway. The compass direction is rounded up or down to the nearest ten degrees, and the last digit lopped off. This then becomes the 'name' for each end of the runway. In Diagram 7, the runway is '09' at one end, and '27' at the other, which corresponds to a compass bearing of 90/270 degrees magnetic. An approaching aircraft is told which end is the 'Active Runway', where the pilot must land. If the wind is predominantly westerly, then 'Runway 27' is the active one, and aircraft will take-off and land at that end of it.

Runway Navigation Aids

Runways are equipped with various landing aids to assist a pilot. Most landing aircraft will use the runway's Instrument Landing System (ILS)

DIAGRAM 7. RUNWAY LAYOUT.

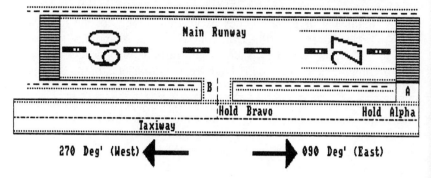

flying the aircraft down the radio beams either manually, or by coupling the aircraft's autopilot to the ILS for an automatic landing.

Taxiways are access 'roads' leading from the airport's apron area, where the aircraft park to embark/disembark passengers, to the runway or runways (see Diagram 7). They are a vital part of the runway system, and often have sophisticated lighting systems, marking the centreline with green lights, and the edges with blue. At hold points, or where taxiways cross, a double line of red lights controls the crossing point. These lights are 'fail-safe': they are left at red until an aircraft calls for permission to cross, when they then change to white. After the aircraft has crossed the lights revert to red again.

Precision Approach Path Indicators – PAPIs

The PAPIs' lights assist pilots on final approach (see Diagram 8). The lamps are fitted with specially designed lenses which indicate the correct descent profile of 3 degrees visually to an aircraft coming in to land. Some airports use the older, and not so accurate, VASI lights which consist of two, or sometimes three rows of three lamps either side of the runway. Correct descent profile is indicated by red-over-white lights.

Runway Maintenance

There are a variety of airport vehicles designed especially for work on the runway. During daily use, rubbish builds up; debris from surrounding areas gets blown onto the runway, various bits and bobs tend to fall off aircraft due to the strong vibration levels experienced on take-off

Diagram 8. PAPI & VASIS.

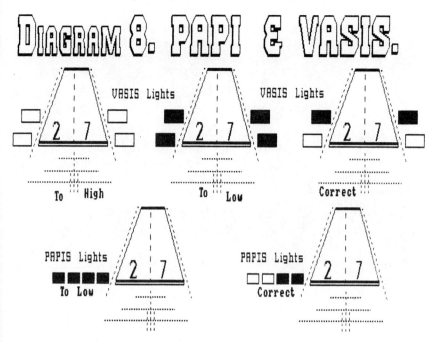

and landing, and damage to the runway's surface can occur. A sweeper vehicle makes regular trips up and down the runway, sweeping it clean. A magnetic bar trailed behind the truck picks up the odd nut and bolt. In winter, snowploughs get rid of snow while a de-icer truck sprays the surface with a thin coating of antifreeze, to help keep it clear. Yet another runway vehicle makes regular checks on the runway's surface grip, directly measuring the amount of friction. When the surface grip falls below a certain level, the runway is given another anti-slip coating.

Aircraft Parking

In the bad old days, aircraft parked out on the apron area, and passengers were bussed (if they were lucky) out to them, boarding by steps. Often they had to walk to the aircraft. At some regional airports passengers still have to walk to the aircraft, but thankfully, the apron and stands are now much nearer to the departures lounge, so the journey isn't very far. Larger airports have a pier arrangement where aircraft park nose-in.

A covered walkway extends from the pier to the doors of the aircraft, and passengers board the plane this way. Once all passengers have been loaded, the aircraft needs the services of an airport tug to push the plane

Piers and walkways at Manchester Airport

back, away from the pier, to face a taxiway. The aircraft then uses its own engines to journey to the runway.

A few British airports have recently built 'Satellite Piers' which are circular buildings around the circumference of which the aircraft park, again, nose-in. A telescopic walkway links the aircraft to the satellite pier, along which the passengers board the aircraft. The advantage of the satellite pier is it gives aircraft more turning space, and more can be fitted in, requiring less space than a straight pier.

Airport Vehicles

The airport's apron area can often be a very busy place indeed. To 'turn' an aircraft around – re-stock, refuel etc. for its return journey – requires the help of many different services and vehicles. In flight, jet engines run the generators which supply the aircraft with electrical power. On the ground, the engines are turned off. Electrical power, to maintain the aircraft's air conditioning system, refrigerators etc. is supplied externally, from a GPU – Ground Power Unit, which is usually a diesel generator mounted onto a truck chassis for mobility around the apron area. The GPU sometimes has an air compressor as well, for starting the aircraft's jet engines.

Passengers' baggage is transported out to the aircraft on a baggage tug, which is a small vehicle – often battery powered – towing a row of trailers. At the aircraft, another vehicle with a conveyor belt transports the luggage from the baggage tug into the aircraft's hold.

Some airports have a system of fuel pipes beneath the surface, with outlets via hydrants at the piers. When the aircraft needs to take on fuel, a pump vehicle drives out to the aircraft, connects the input of the pump to the fuel hydrant and starts pumping the jet fuel into the aircraft. Smaller airports don't have this customised fuel distribution system, and use the familiar fuel tankers, or 'bowsers' as they are called.

Aircraft carry cargo as well as passengers, so you'll often see another tug towing a train of either custom-designed containers, which are profiled to fit exactly into an aircraft's cargo hold, or pallets of cargo. Actual loading into the aircraft's hold is done by the conveyor belt for small items or a fork-lift truck for the containers and larger cargo.

Of course, food and drink used on the outward journey has to be replenished for the return trip. Catering trucks, with specially designed extending bodies, bring the food and drink out to the aircraft. When in the correct position, the body of the truck lifts up on scissor-action extending jacks, to the height of the loading doors, and the trolleys containing the prepared meals are wheeled straight into the aircraft and stored.

A water tanker brings fresh drinking and washing water out to the aircraft, and pumps it into the potable water storage tanks on board. Similarly, the effluent from the toilets and washbasins has to be removed from the aircraft. The delightfully named Honey Cart, another type of tanker, collects this waste and removes it to the sewerage disposal point.

Although the crew (Pilot and First Officer) always perform a walk-round, visual inspection of the aircraft before every flight, if they find a problem they can't deal with it themselves. A maintenance crew, assuming that the fault is a minor one, will come out to the aircraft and rectify it. Transport for them is usually an airport Land-Rover.

Finally, a small minibus will transport the aircraft's crew out to the aircraft. Where passengers are still bussed out to the planes, to assist them getting on, a truck with steps, or Airstairs as they are called, will travel out to the aircraft and position the stairs under the plane's passenger entrance doors.

Ground Movement Control

That's some fifteen vehicles of various types involved just with turning an aircraft around. Added to this number must be all the other trucks, tugs and carts which travel around the airport manoeuvering area, such as the runway sweeper truck, security and bird patrols, fire service,

Ground Movement Control Tower, Manchester Airport

marshalling vehicle and airport maintenance cars. All these vehicles are designed especially for the job they do. For example, Push-Back tugs are built specially low so that they can fit underneath the aircraft. Catering trucks have bodies which can extend up to the height of an aircraft's loading doors. Organising and coordinating movement of all these vehicles is vital if accidents are to be avoided, and the person who controls all activity around the airport manoeuvering area is the Ground Movement Controller – great name, isn't it!

All airport vehicle drivers have special training in radio telephony techniques and tuition on their vehicles' special handling requirements. Their vehicles are equipped with radio transceivers which they use to talk to the Ground Movement Controller, or Ground as the job is called over radio. Airport vehicles tend to use their job title as their radio callsign. For example. 'Sweeper 1' for the runway sweeper truck, 'Bird-Alpha' – or, in one particular case, 'Seagull' – for the airport's busy bird patrol unit. There is a list of the frequency ranges used by ground and airport service vehicles in the Radiodatabase section.

The Ground Movement Controller works in the Visual Control Room of the airport's control tower, alongside the Aerodrome Controller, known as 'Tower'. Basically, Tower looks after the runway, coordinating take-offs and landings. Ground and Tower work closely together, so that Ground can arrange the safe movement of vehicles.

For example, if Tower receives reports from pilots of debris on the runway, she may ask Ground to call the sweeper truck to clear away the rubbish. Ground calls the sweeper truck on his UHF radio, and instructs it to clear the runway. Obviously, the driver of the sweeper truck would take a very dim view of any pilot who tried to land a DC10 on top of his vehicle, so Tower ensures that no aircraft will attempt to use the runway while the sweeper is doing its thing. Once the job's complete, 'Sweeper 1' will call Ground and tell him that the runway is now back to its usual pristine condition, and that his truck is clear of the area. Ground informs Tower that the runway's clear, and that she can start using it again.

The same system applies to any airport vehicle. Where it has to cross a taxiway or the runway, it must stop, ask for permission, execute the crossing and then report that the crossing has been done, and the taxiway etc. is once again clear. Ground also has responsibility for the lighting system around the airport, including the runway.

Who Owns What

All these 'apron services' can be provided either by the airport authorities directly, the individual airline companies or third party companies specialising in this area. In practice, what tends to happen is that apron services are provided by a mixture of all three. For example, at Luton Airport, where Britannia Airways has its head office, they have a maintenance facility for their aircraft. They also handle maintenance for other airlines as well as their own. Similarly, where an airline has its own booking-in, baggage handling and passenger services operation at an airport, they will undertake the same work for other airlines who don't have a base at that airport, and would find it uneconomical to maintain their own operation.

Servisair Limited

The third-party handling agents, of which Servisair is the country's leading example, specialise in providing a range of airport services. They don't actually run an airline at all, own no aircraft and employ no pilots. What they do is provide a complete airport service for any airline company requesting its services, from passenger handling staff, in their smart blue uniforms, ground handling staff, providing a complete range of apron services, to the people who clean the inside of an aircraft on turn-around. Servisair employs some 2,300 people and provide services for various airlines at 18 UK airports, 2 Irish, and a further 27 airports in Europe.

In the Airband Radio and Radiodatabases sections, you'll see various references to 'Company Frequencies'. Pilots often need to communicate directly with either their parent company, or handling agents, using radio telephony. Such messages concern things like estimated arrival/departure times, victual requirements at destination airports and any special passenger requirements, such as wheelchairs, nursing aid etc.

Passenger Facilities

Airports have to cater for everyone; from the businesswoman and man, with their special requirements of late check-in times, enough space in the terminal and on the plane to work, to the 'bucket-and-spade' holiday travellers, who quite rightly declare themselves 'on holiday' the moment they arrive at the airport.

Terminal buildings have changed enormously in the past twenty years to reflect this diversity of the travelling public. And yet, airports do have this rather odd atmosphere, often acting as a magnet, drawing in the undesirable, as well as the big-spending, 'I'm on holiday – where's the bar?' travellers. Some of the weirdest conversations and strangest people I've ever met have been at airports in the UK!

Most regional airports have just the one terminal building which handles both arrivals and departures. Manchester International has an *International* and a *Domestic* terminal: Heathrow has four terminals. On arrival at the airport, passengers make for the check-in desks where they are relieved of their baggage, and issued with the necessary paperwork to actually get them onto the aircraft. Once they've checked-in, they are free to mill around until their flight is called.

Once the flight is called, passengers head for Passport Control, and Immigration and thence into the Departures Lounge, which forms the interface between *Landside* and *Airside*. Once in the Departures Lounge, passengers are technically no longer in Britain, and can now have access to duty free shops. For arrivals, the passengers leave the aircraft and make for Baggage Reclaim, where they collect their luggage etc. From Baggage Reclaim they then pass through Immigration, Passport and Health control, and into the Customs and Excise area. Once through Customs the passengers once again re-cross the interface from Airside to Landside, and back again to grey skies and drizzle!

Airports often seem to be places of frantic activity, with people and vehicles dashing around apparently at random. Nothing could be further from the truth. The Airline Dispatchers have carefully worked out plans for each aircraft under their control. They know exactly what it needs and when it needs it, and they ensure that it gets it too! Aircraft cost millions of pounds to purchase, and many more millions to keep them in the air. An aircraft parked is spending, not earning. Therefore all airline companies work their aircraft hard, keeping them where they belong – up in the sky. Of course this doesn't mean that the aircraft are mistreated; quite the contrary. Because they are worked so hard they are so well looked after.

Often, at an airport, it's worth ignoring the aircraft for a while and just concentrate on the events unfolding on the apron area. Add the relevant UHF company frequency, and a suitable airband receiver, and you'll hear the aircraft dispatcher giving out his or her orders as well.

HEATHROW AIRPORT. KEY 1

The airport key number, as in *Heathrow Key 1, Gatwick, Key 2* etc. refers directly to Appendix 9 – *Airport, Aircraft & ICAO Codes*. What it does is to tell you which airport various airline companies use. For example, East Midlands Airport – Key 9. Looking at Appendix 9 this tells you that the following companies use this airport, Aer Lingus, Air 2000, Air Europa, Air Europe, Air Malta, and so on.

Heathrow! The busiest airport in the world, built upon ground trodden by the hooves of Black Bess as a certain Mr R. Turpin plied his dubious trade where the airport's northern perimeter is now. The site where the last wolf in England was slain, where pagan Saxon temples were once revered; and the former marshes where strange *Will O' Wisp* lights lured the unwary into robbery and violent death. Glorius Heathrow! Home of Concorde.

Heathrow is unique amongst British airports, apart from being the busiest in the world that is. For Heathrow is the *only* UK air terminal with parallel runways capable of handling any of today's jetliners. One runway is used for landings: the other for take-offs, with a changeover at 1500 hours each day to give the local residents a little relief from the virtually continuous aircraft movements. Runway use is planned weekly, so that wear and tear on the surface (and on local residents' nerves) is evened out.

Runways

The whole airport complex covers nearly 3,000 acres, which is encased within 10 miles of perimeter road, which itself surrounds a total of nearly 50 miles of internal roadways. Just think what a prime, 3,000 acre site in London would cost today! Heathrow has three runways. The parallels are: 27R/09L and 27L/09R. The 'Right' and 'Left' refers to the direction the pilot is facing on coming into land. Runway 27R/09L is 12,800 feet long by 150 feet wide (3902 x 45 metres); while 27L/09R is slightly shorter at 12,000 feet by 150 feet (3658 x 45 metres). The third runway, 05/23, is also the smallest, being 7734 feet long by 150 feet wide (2357 x 45 metres).

Airport Layout

Heathrow splits nicely into two main parts; the central area, and everything else. The outer part of the central area is made up from Terminals 1, 2 and 3, plus the Queen's building. Terminal 4 is a good distance away from the central area, to the south, near the '05' end of runway 05/23.

Spectator Facilities

The roof gardens of Terminal 2 and the Queen's building are the main viewing areas at Heathrow, which give good views of the three runways and Terminals 1, 2 and 3's aircraft stands. There are the usual cafes and eating places, plus a book/sweet shop and an Airshop which sells aviation related goods. There are no flight announcements or information VDUs on the roof gardens.

A charge is made for use of the spectator area, but do remember that multi-storey car park roofs, laybys at the ends of runways etc. sometimes provide a better viewing option depending on what you're after.

Spectator area, Heathrow Airport (*reproduced by kind permission of the BAA – Heathrow*)

Just remember not to cause a nuisance by parking your car in a silly place – I might want to get past you!

Spotters often come a long way for a day's viewing at Heathrow. The spectator areas are open every day, 9.30 am to 6 pm in summer, 9.30 am to 4.30 pm in winter, except Christmas and Boxing days, and a phone call before you leave home will bring peace of mind for the journey. Telephone 081 745 7115. Heathrow's Central Bus Station has a direct footpath linking the Queen's building and Terminal 2, so access for spotters is quite simple. Should you be brave enough to face driving to Heathrow, you'll find the long-stay car parking at Terminals 1, 2 and 3 a fraction of the cost of short-term parking.

Getting There

Heathrow has two Underground railway stations, both on the *Piccadilly* line. Average journey time into London is around 45 minutes, and

Central Terminal Area

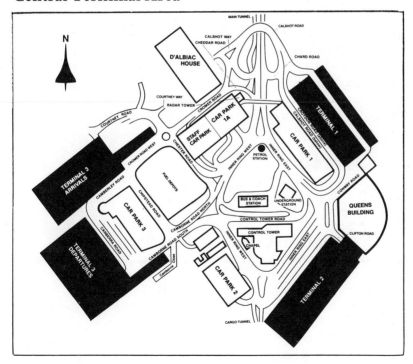

Central area map, Heathrow Airport (*reproduced by kind permission of the BAA – Heathrow*)

trains run at 3-minute intervals during peak hours, dropping to 10 minutes off-peak. A moving walkway system connects the Underground stations to Terminals 1, 2 and 3. There are numerous coach and bus services, often running directly from cities all over the country into Heathrow's Central Bus Station, or various terminals. There is the usual service from London Victoria Coach Station direct to the airport. It is perfectly feasible for a Yorkshire-based plane spotter to hop onto a coach in Leeds, and de-bus outside Terminal 3, around four (oops: M25!) to six hours later.

For drivers, make sure you know which terminal you want! Terminals 1, 2 and 3 are in the central area, and access is via the tunnel from the Bath Road, or the M4. Spotters wanting Terminal 4 (coming from outside of London) need to be on the M25, leaving at Junction 14, the Terminal 4 exit (clearly signposted). Apart from that, it's the usual job – aim the car south down the M1, remembering to get your visa stamped at Watford Gap if you're not from the Home Counties, M25 and then follow the signs for Heathrow.

Aircraft and ATC

As already explained, Heathrow is the busiest airport in the world, with an aircraft taking-off or landing around once a minute at busy times. The beginner can do little but look and gasp with awe at all this activity. However, to help you along Radiodatabase 1 lists British Airport ATC frequencies, while Appendix 9 lists which airlines use what airports. This applies to all airports discussed in the Handbook.

GATWICK AIRPORT. KEY 2

Gatwick was officially opened in June 1958, after an eight million-pound conversion from its familiar metamorphosis of private aerodrome, RAF base – civil airport. It now boasts a satellite pier, giving the airport a very distinct American look and a new terminal building. It is rated the second busiest air terminal in the world, behind Heathrow, and has a current throughput of some eighteen million passengers a year; which isn't bad going at all considering that Gatwick handles few scheduled flights in comparison to their huge charter operations! Gatwick is owned and run by the British Airports Authority (BAA).

There are two passenger terminals at Gatwick: the North Terminal and the two hundred-million pound investment in the new South Terminal. A system of pathways and a fast ferry service provide means of travel between the two widely spaced terminals. The ferry service is actually a driverless 'train' with three carriages holding around sixty passengers in total, which takes around two minutes for the journey. But wheelchair users will have to wheel along the walkways, as trying to get a chair onto the shuttle is definitely unfunny.

The Runway

Gatwick's single runway is 10,165 feet long (3098 metres) by 150 feet wide (45 metres), and so can handle just about any current aircraft type. The directions are: 26/08, with Runway two-six being used most of the time in the prevailing westerly winds. The question of another runway for Gatwick is raised around every holiday season! The biggest problem is that parallel runways, as at Heathrow, must have a minimum separation of 150 metres for concurrent working.

There isn't space at Gatwick for this, which leaves the question up in the air. It's solely due to superb airport management and ATC procedures that Gatwick is the world's number 2 airport, considering it only has the one runway. In the US there are airports with four, five, even six! If passenger numbers continue to increase as they have done in the past, and there's absolutely no reason why they shouldn't; then Gatwick must have another runway. Either the rules will have to be changed to allow a number 2 runway, or someone's going to have to build (yet) another London airport; only this time it's going to cost billions instead of millions!

Spectator Facilities

Gatwick is justly famous for its caring and enthusiastic attitude to the plane spotter – or just the idle viewer. Many plane spotters actually prefer it to the rather more chaotic Heathrow! There is an excellent observation deck on the roof of the South Terminal (access via the Arrival's Concourse), which has catering facilities, covered viewing areas in the cafeteria (use the special seating), a public telephone, book and sweetshop, and an Airshop. The view of the manoeuvering area is very good, and presents good photographic opportunities without having to use long telephoto lenses.

On the spectator observation deck there are PA announcements for flights and also arrival/departure VDUs – so you can stay under cover during inclement weather, and only dash outside for that particular photo you want!

A new and rather novel feature is the introduction of Gatwick Radio, the airport's very own radio broadcasting station on frequency 1584kHz in the Medium Wave band. Give it a listen next time you're down (up?) there (Heathrow also has the same facility, by the way).

There is a token charge for using the spectators gallery (around 60p

– Oct. '90), and it is open every day, 8 am to 8 pm except for Christmas and Boxing days. If you're travelling a long way, (and you'd be amazed at where some spotters travel from!) it's always best to check that the gallery is open first. Call them on 0293 503843.

Disabled spotters are very well catered for by Gatwick. Wheelchair users should head for multi-storey car park number 3, which is the nearest one to the International Arrivals concourse, South Terminal, and use the lifts from the ground level to level 4, the spectators viewing area. There is no charge to disabled plane spotters.

Getting There

At BAA airports – which after all are some of the busiest in the world – it is not a good idea to drive there directly. In almost all cases, the expense of airport short-term car parking will be more than it would cost to leave your car away from the terminal and use public transport. Of course, I do recognise that some of us have to use cars, and that you have to visit during the busy periods too; all told, a recipe for disaster!

Gatwick has a wide choice of public transport options. There is a British Rail station (at the South Terminal end) which has lift as well as escalator access to the platforms. The station naturally connects to the whole BR rail system nationwide. The airport runs a special bus service every fifteen minutes during the day – and every hour at night – from the main terminal area to the Victoria Rail Station in London. Express coach services also link Heathrow and Luton airports with Gatwick, and a Gatwick Airport coach service runs from London's Victoria Coach Station which is around half-a-mile from Victoria Rail Station. As Victoria Coach Station is the termini for many coaches across the country, travel by this method isn't such a bad idea.

Access for drivers is simple enough. Aim the car at London, onto the M25, onto the M23 and exit at Junction 9 for Gatwick. There are covered walkways from the short-term car parks to the terminals, and a free bus shuttle service connects long-stay car parking with the North and South terminals. Be warned! Airports in general (and Gatwick/ Heathrow specifically) DO NOT recognise the national disabled Orange Badge scheme. Leave your car anywhere other than the official public car parks and you'll be towed away, and face a really nasty 'fine' to recover the car.

PRESTWICK INTERNATIONAL AIRPORT. KEY 3

Prestwick Airport grew from the initial flying school started by an RAF Group Captain and a duke, who were the first people to fly over Mount

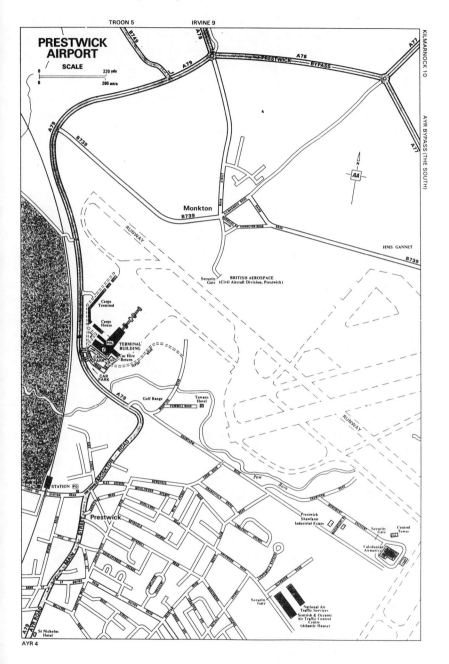

Prestwick Airport map (*reproduced by kind permission of the BAA – Prestwick*)

Everest, to its present day international facility. Prestwick is the only Scottish airport authorised by the CAA for non-stop transatlantic flights. It's owned and run by the British Airports Authority, and can handle any future passenger increases without major modifications to either runway or terminal areas.

Apart from being an International airport Prestwick is also home to SCATCC – the Scottish Air Traffic Control Centre, and Shanwick Oceanic Air Traffic Control Centre, based within Atlantic House. Altogether, a very bustling place for air traffic control activities, as well as its daily flight schedules.

Runway

Prestwick's main runway is 13/31, at 9,100 feet long, (2,987 metres) by 150 feet wide (45 metres). The second runway is designated 03/21 and is smaller than the main runway, at 5,600 feet (1,829 metres).

Spectator Facilities

The spectator terrace is situated on the roof of the main terminal, and offers good views of the stands and the runways. It's open from 7.00 am to 6.00 pm in the summer months, and 8.00 am to 5.00 pm in winter.

Getting There

Prestwick airport is around 15 miles from Ayr on the beautiful Western coast of Scotland, and is just 26 miles south/west of Glasgow. There is ample short and long stay car parking at the airport, and regular coach services from Glasgow and Ayr.

MANCHESTER AIRPORT. KEY 4

Previously known as Ringway, Manchester International is the fastest growing airport in the world. With over 70 operators flying 154 routes, 200 tour operators and some 11 million passengers handled in 1989, you begin to get a feel for this popular, Northern airport. New buildings are springing up almost around the clock as the airport authorities plan for new growth. Recently completed is the £27 million UK Domestic Terminal A. On-going at the moment are the World Freight Terminal – completion scheduled for 1991 – a dedicated rail link to Manchester city centre and British Rail's National network, to commence in 1991.

The new, new terminal, the £550 million International Terminal 2, is scheduled to open Phase 1 in 1993. When I was last there in October '90, the steel structure was almost finished, and work had started on the exterior. It's going to be very big, boosting airport passenger handling to some 16 million per year!

Apart from the airport facility, Manchester is also home to the Manchester Terminal Control Area (MTMA) which acts as an ATCC sub-centre for LATCC, looking after the ATC for aircraft below 15,500 feet. Manchester ATC sub-centre is housed in the tower building.

Runway

Manchester has just the one runway. It's 10,000 feet (3,048 metres) long by 150 feet (45 metres) wide, and is designated 06/24, with '24' being the usual active end. Both ends have displaced thresholds. The runway has a maximum usage of 40 movements (landings or take-offs) per hour, and can often actually reach this figure. Manchester is an ICAO Catagory E 'All Weather' airport, with a CAA 3b ILS category rating.

Spectator Facilities

Manchester's spectator facilities are in the hands of the local aviation society – TAS – which has its base there. There is spectator terracing on top of the International Terminal, for which there is no charge. On the terracing there is an Airshop, selling airband radio receivers and Scanners, aviation books, magazines and maps, model aeroplane kits, binoculars etc. A kiosk provides hot and cold drinks, as well as snack food such as crisps and chocolate bars. Both the Airshop and the kiosk, as well as the airport tour centre, are run by TAS, more of which in a while.

Manchester Airport is not so kind as others are where disabled plane spotters and, in particular, wheelchair users are concerned. Access to the spectator terracing is only via two sets of (lethal when wet) metal stairs. There are NO lifts up to this area and, short of being carried, there is no access for wheelchair users at all!

However, there is a multi-storey short-stay car park with an open roof level. In actual fact, this offers better views of departing aircraft than the official spectator terracing. Unfortunately for wheelchair users, this level is surrounded by a boundary wall whose top just happens to be at eye level when you're sat in your chair!

There is a good view of the apron area, and the international pier from the Airside bar and buffet in Terminal B Departures main concourse, and also from the cafeteria between Terminal B and A, but you have to be eating or drinking as the price of your seat.

Getting There

Access to the airport by road is quite simple, via the direct link M56 straight into the terminal. This motorway also interfaces with the north/

south M6, and the east/west M62, providing access from wherever in the country you're coming from. A direct rail link is planned for the future, and there are regular coach services into Manchester, Salford and surrounding areas, as well as direct coach links with many cities around the country.

There is a multi-storey car park for short-stay parking, but for visits over four hours it's much cheaper to use either of the long-stay car parks (currently £2.80 for 24 hours, October, '90). A free shuttle bus service transports people from/to the long-stay parks, but hang-on tightly! Whatever you do, you must make a note of the long-term car park area and row number where you left your vehicle. Speaking from personal experience, it's embarrassing if you don't. I certainly never realised just how popular white Ford Fiestas are! The usual rules apply regarding vehicles left in prohibited areas, and the Orange Badge scheme doesn't apply either.

The Aviation Society (TAS)

TAS is one of the organisations I mentioned earlier. It has some 2,500 current members, and is based at Manchester airport. TAS produces an excellent monthly newsletter, *Winged Words*, in A5 format with photographs and the latest news from the aviation world. Naturally, a lot of the information concerns Manchester, details such as any special aircraft visiting the terminal, information about over-flights etc. They also arrange airport tours for members and non-members, as well as organising excursions for members to various airports and air traffic control centres both at home and abroad, as well as special flights. Telephone 061 499 0303 for information about tours or TAS.

GLASGOW AIRPORT. KEY 5

Glasgow Airport came into being literally overnight! In 1966 the change from former Royal Navy Fleet Air Arm station to Glasgow Airport was accomplished within the hours of darkness, ready for the first flight arrival the following morning at 8.00 am. The terminal is run by the British Airports Authority, and is currently handling some 3 million passengers a year.

Runways

Glasgow has two. The main runway, 05/23 is 8,100 feet (2,658 metres) long, and the second runway, 10/28 is smaller at 3,320 feet (1,088 metres), and is used for light aircraft only. Both runways have ILS. There is a single passenger terminal, one Domestic and one International pier.

Spectator Facilities

There aren't any: we're not welcome! There is the odd view of the apron area from windows in the terminal building, but your best chances come from roads etc. around the perimeter of the airport. But do be careful where you leave your vehicle. There is a multi-storey car park to the west of the terminal building, and you could try your chances from there.

Getting There

British Rail's National network feeds into Paisley Gilmour Street Station, which is Glasgow Airport's nearest rail link. Regular coach services link the terminal with Glasgow's main bus and coach stations, and there's a direct coach link route into Edinburgh. Drivers need the M8 motorway, and should exit at Junction 28.

LONDON CITY AIRPORT. KEY 6

Rising phoenix-like, quite literally from the ashes of the old London docks, is Britain's newest airport, London City, or Lucy as it is nicknamed, from the callsign of its NDB, 'LCY'. The whole concept and implementation of this airport belongs to the John Mowlem company, who felt that there should be air connections between the city of London and other major areas within a 400-mile radius.

To meet the maximum permitted aircraft noise level requirements for a city centre airport, only certain types of aeroplane could be utilised. Brymon Airways, with their fleet of DHC Dash 7s fitted in ideally. The Dash 7 is a very quiet turbo-prop aircraft which could cover the intended operational range with ease, and has STOL – Short Take-Off and Landing ability, which, as London City's only runway is just half a mile long, is most convenient.

The two main airline operators are Brymon Airways, and London City Airways, using mainly DHC Dash 7s. The airport ATC navigation aids are 'state-of-the-art' and quite unique. Whereas the standard glide slope for an airport ILS is 3 degrees, because of London City's location and difficult approach, Racal Avionics had to design and build an Instrument Landing System to cope with a glide slope of 7½ degrees.

At the time of writing, trials using the brilliant British Aerospace's BAe 146 Whisper Jet, the quietest jet-powered aircraft in the world, are taking place with a view to extending the range of operations over the present 400-mile radius. However, even though the BAe 146 has STOL capabilities, it will still mean London City extending the runway, assuming that the relevant permissions are granted, of course.

Runway

London City's single runway, designated 10/28, is some 2,640 feet (762 metres) long.

Spectator Facilities

There aren't any, really. This is a business person's airport, so very little time is spent on just looking. There are views available from the upper levels of the very swish terminal building, but as there are only the two airline companies, both of which use the DHC Dash 7, interest quickly wanes!

Getting There

Access is fairly easy via the M11, M25 motorways. The Docklands Light Railway system is extending eastwards, removing the present two-mile hike, and providing a direct link to the airport.

LIVERPOOL AIRPORT. KEY 7

Liverpool International Airport was built on the site of the old RAF station; more importantly, unlike most other regional airports which retained their RAF-built runways etc. it was designed and constructed as a civil airport from the outset, something it shares with Gatwick, which are the only two purpose-built civil airports in the UK. It has a new tower, fire station and terminal buildings, an improved and extended runway, and a new Royal Mail Sorting Office which already handles some seventeen per cent of the country's mail. A new cargo terminal is presently under construction, and as each improvement is made, more aviation-based companies are attracted to the airport, establishing their operations permanently.

Runway

Liverpool's single runway, designated 09/27 is 7,500 feet (2,286 metres) long, and can handle most current aircraft types. It has ILS and PAPIs.

Spectator Facilities

Plane spotters are very welcome at Liverpool. There are a great number of cargo and mail flights using the airport so there's plenty to see. Telephone 051 486 8877 for further information.

Getting There

Outside of Liverpool, main access is via the M6, M62 and M56 motorways, with the relevant junctions well signposted. There are frequent coach services from the airport into the city.

BIRMINGHAM AIRPORT. KEY 8

Although there's been an airport of some type or other on the site since the late 1930s the present Birmingham International Airport came into being in 1987. It is owned and run by the seven local Metropolitan District Councils, with ATC and telecommunications leased from the CAA.

The new main terminal lies to the south-east of the airport, and is itself a really nice building, very light and airy. To keep pace with the increased passenger and freight growth, which is currently running at 3 million passengers handled per year, and over 31,000 tonnes of cargo worth in excess of £700 million, a new terminal building is under construction, with completion scheduled for 1991. Birmingham Airport's new control tower is very futuristic looking, and offers a much better view across the manoeuvering area than the old tower in the (presently disused) 1930s terminal building.

The existing freight depot on the opposite side of the airport to the passenger terminal is also scheduled for major extension. Freight West as the new cargo terminal will be named, will have dedicated taxiways and aircraft stands for aeroplanes, including the Boeing 747s. Plus of course the administration, Customs etc. to cope with the increased business.

Being sited alongside the National Exhibition Centre produces a lot of exhibition freight and passenger traffic. A unique Maglev monorail-type train links the airport to the nearby British Rail International station and the National Exhibition Centre. Maglev is a magnetically levitated carriage, which can ferry 40 passengers over the 660 metre journey in 90 seconds flat!

Runways

Birmingham has two. The main runway, 15/33 is 7,400 feet (2,255 metres) long, whilst the smaller 02/24 is 4,315 feet (1,315 metres). Both runways are 150 feet (45 metres) wide. Runway 15/33 has a category 2 ILS, 02/24 is used for general (light) aviation traffic and has no ILS.

Entrance, Birmingham Airport (*reproduced by kind permission of the Birmingham Airport Authority*)

Spectator Facilities

There are some airports you instinctively feel at home with. Birmingham is one of them. The airport authorities have gone a long way towards welcoming spotters and this is self-evident in the spectator area.

A lift from the outside ground level of the new terminal building transports you up to the spectators gallery on the first floor. There is a nominal charge, 30p at the time of writing, an aviation hobby shop, buffet and toilets. The gallery is open from 7.30 am to 9.30 pm in the summer; and 8 am to 9 pm in winter every day of the year except Christmas Day. Telephone 021 767 7243 for further information.

Short-stay car park 1 is the nearest car park to the terminal building. Charges are £1.90 up to 4 hours, and £3.20 for up to 8. There is a multi-storey car park behind the terminal building, but it isn't much use to spotters because the terminal actually blocks much of the airside view. Charge for the long-term car park is £1.40 for up to 12 hours.

Disabled people's facilities at Birmingham are superb, and very well thought-out indeed. There's an Induction Loop system for those with hearing difficulties, touch-maps for the sight restricted, and lifts for wheelchair users. There are disabled persons' toilets, and several public telephones positioned at wheelchair height. Well done Birmingham!

Getting There

Access by road is well served, with the M1, M5, M6 and M42 motorways. All exit junctions for the airport are well signposted. The Maglev People Mover offers a direct link to BR International station at the NEC, which then links you to the national rail network. Coaches run directly into the airport from central Birmingham. There are also many direct coach links nationwide, again running into the airport.

EAST MIDLANDS AIRPORT. KEY 9

Although the East Midlands International Airport is built on the site of a disused RAF base, virtually nothing left by the service was of much use. Therefore, East Midlands, or Castle Donnington as I always think of it, was rebuilt in the 1960s.

It opened for service in 1965, and has since built up a healthy schedule and charter service plus a thriving air cargo operation, based in the custom-built cargo centre. British Midland Airways and Air Bridge Carriers have both made East Midlands their operational base. Recognising that plane spotters bring a fair amount of revenue to the terminal, the airport authorities have really gone to town with spectator and visitor features and facilities; more of which in a while.

Runway

The single runway, designated 09/27 is 7,500 feet (2,286 metres) long and 150 feet (45 metres) wide. It is equipped with ILS and PAPIs, with

'27' being the usual, active end. It can handle most of the current jetliners, and I well remember the first time a Boeing 747 landed there (it did it with consummate ease, too!). There are 2 LOM – Locator Outer Marker – beacons at East Midlands. EME, at the eastern end of the runway, and EMW, at the western end.

Spectator Facilities

Nothing short of superb! There is a viewing balcony in the main terminal building, level 2, which offers good views of aircraft taxying from/to the apron and stands, and aircraft rotating on take-off. Access to the upper level in the terminal building is either via stairs or a lift. A large cafeteria with wide windows runs parallel to this balcony, so if the weather turns a little chill you can go inside into the warmth and still retain the view.

East Midlands also has the 12-acre Aeropark, which is a part of the airport at the '27' end of the runway given over entirely to the aviation enthusiast. There are static examples of various aircraft in roped-off areas, including my all-time favourite, the Argosy Transport. This particular one on display I used to watch in the early seventies, flying in and out of East Midlands; it's nice to know it was saved from the breakers!

There is a Visitors Centre housed within a very modern (and warm!) building which has permanent displays of aviation material, including a superb scale model of the airport's layout. There are various static examples of jet engines and a shop selling aviation-related goods. Also within the Visitors Centre is a lecture theatre – the airport does a roaring trade in school visits. There are very clean toilets near to the Visitors Centre building, including a unisex one for disabled people. And to keep the children happy, there's an adventure playground, with a specially laid floor of soft tree bark mulch, so accidental falls are well cushioned.

Saving the best to last, the Aeropark gives you just about the best view of incoming aircraft of any British airport. You are exactly *180 metres* from the threshold of the active runway! Even closer to the taxiway. You can actually feel the ground shaking beneath your feet as a 757 trundles along the taxiway to join Runway 27 at Hold Alpha. Watching a Short's 360, BAe 146 or a DHC Dash 7 approach the threshold at something like 60 feet, and then simply plonk down right in front of your eyes is really something!

Photographers will rarely need more than a 135mm lens to fill the frame. Liberally scattered along the raised banking of the spectator area are picnic tables, there is usually a kiosk open for business, selling hot food and drinks, cold drinks and sandwiches. Access to the Aeropark is through automatic barriers, and admission charge is currently £1 for a car or minibus, and £8 for a coach. You feed the barrier with a coin and go through.

The Visitors Centre building is open all year round, except for the period December 25th to January 1st. It opens 10 am until 5 pm Monday to Friday, and 11 am to 6 pm weekends during the months 1st April to 31st October. From November 1st to 31st March, the Centre opens 11 am to 4 pm Monday to Sunday. The Aeropark is open virtually anytime. Telephone 0332 810621 for further information.

Getting There

Access is via the M1 motorway from anywhere in the country, leaving it at Junction 24. The airport is around 3 miles from this junction. At the time of writing there's some really heavy roadworks going on at Junction 24 as new access roads are being laid. During peak times this causes long delays, so if you're driving there, avoid travelling during peak hours. Coach services link the airport directly with Nottingham, Leicester and Derby. There is ample short- and long-term car parking, and special reserved places for disabled people.

LEEDS/BRADFORD AIRPORT. KEY 10

Leeds/Bradford has a very long and difficult history. During the war, Yeadon was taken over by the RAF. Across the other side of the airfield, the A.V.Roe Aircraft factory was busy turning out Anson, Lancaster, and Lincoln bombers, which needed hard runways. So the present day two-runway system was laid down. An appeal in 1969 to extend runway 14/32 by 2,000 feet was rejected.

The new terminal building, together with a new freight depot, was opened in 1968. Due to the rapid increase in the terminal's IT (Inclusive Tour) business during the seventies, another appeal to extend runway 14/32 was made in 1979. After a public inquiry, permission was granted to extend – but at a price. The government nailed the Leeds/Bradford airport operator's feet to the runway, by placing horrendously severe restrictions on the airport's operations and its opening hours.

A £20 million rebuilding plan resulted in an increase of 2,500 feet to runway 14/32, an extension to the terminal building, a new cargo centre, improved airport lighting and ATC navigation aids.

Today, Leeds/Bradford handles just under a million passengers and 4,752 tonnes of freight per year, despite the crippling operating restrictions. It has successfully fought and won a partial relaxation of its opening times, but even so, there are still more restrictions on this airport than most other, similar types. The new airport to be built at Sheffield had better look out!

Runways

The main runway, designated 14/32 is 7,400 feet (2,255 metres) and is equipped with ILS and PAPIs. The second runway, 10/280 is around half the length of 13/33 at 3,280 feet (1,000 metres) long. Due to the operating restrictions, runway 14/32 has to be used for most of the time.

Spectator Facilities

Unfortunately, Leeds/Bradford's spectator gallery has just been swallowed up by an extension to the terminal building's passenger catering facilities. Although as far as I'm aware there is no discriminatory policy on plane spotters. It's a case of fitting-in where you'll cause minimum disruption. There are several good viewing positions on the surrounding roads, with handy laybys. Telephone 0532 503431 for further information.

Getting There

Road access is via the M1, M62 motorways, with the relevant exits well signposted. From Bradford you need the A658, and from Leeds the A65 and follow the road signs carefully. Coach services run from Bradford and Leeds directly into the airport. There is ample car parking at the airport and at reasonable prices too.

NEWCASTLE AIRPORT. KEY 11

Newcastle International can trace its roots back to the 1930s, as a grass airfield. However, the statutory take-over by the RAF during the 1940s didn't, in Newcastle's case, produce any benefits in the form of hard-surfaced runways.

In fact, by the time the RAF cleared out of Teesside, almost nothing at all remained. During the 1950s, the main runway began to take shape, and a cluster of buildings provided passenger and freight handling.

The boom in the Inclusive Tour business during the 1960s had the usual effect on this regional airport; a frantic amount of rebuilding resulting in a new pasenger terminal, and the laying of a hard surfaced runway to accommodate current and future aircraft types.

One of the problems Newcastle has to face is its isolated position in respect to the UK airways system. Most British airports are either close to, or literally beneath an airway, and on take-off or landing, they're quickly moved out of airport-controlled airspace into an airway. In Newcastle's case, which doesn't have any nearby airways, to protect aircraft leaving/arriving at the airport, there is a Radar Advisory Service Area surrounding Newcastle's controlled airspace, and for their own safety, all aircraft flying within this area are requested to take part.

The RASA lower limit is 10,500 feet – the airport's Special Rules Area ends at 7,500 feet. To cover the gap between the top of Newcastle's controlled airspace and the RASA lower limit, the airport's radar participate in a Lower Airspace Radar Service (LARS) which provides a radar service to both civil and military aircraft on request. There are many LARS around the London/Scottish FIRs, providing a radar service for aircraft flying VFR outside of controlled airspace.

Runway

Newcastle's single runway, 07/25 is 7,700 feet (2,347 metres) long by 150 feet (45 metres) wide. It has ILS at both ends, and can handle all current aircraft types. '25' is the usual, active runway.

Spectator Facilities

Newcastle welcomes spotters. There's a viewing terrace on top of the terminal building, which is open for most of the year, and offers excellent views of aircraft on take-off. There's a buffet – only open during the summer months – and toilets close at hand. Telephone 091 286 0966 for any information.

Getting There

From Newcastle, join the city's Central Motorway East, leave to join the A696 and then follow the signs. Coach services run every half-hour from the airport directly into the city, and there are some direct, long distance coach services to various UK destinations.

LUTON AIRPORT. KEY 12

Luton Airport, like Gatwick, has established a first-class reputation as a holiday gateway; with Britain's biggest charter airline, Britannia, also the second largest UK airline company overall, making Luton its operational base, along with Monarch Airlines. The airport is wholly

103

owned by the local borough council, and is known by pilots as 'a great little airport'.

The airport's ATC unit is employed directly by the owners and of course, the ATCOs are CAA licensed. They certainly have their work cut out for them too! Luton has a single runway, but no parallel taxiway. A single taxiway splits into two just before meeting the runway, and feeds a point around the centre. This means that a wide-bodied jetliner, such as a DC10, or 747 has to back-track down the runway, and turn itself around ready for take-off. The same applies on landing, with aircraft again having to turn around and return down the runway to access the taxiway.

This adversely affects movements around the manoeuvering area – aircraft having to wait until the runway is cleared – and calls for very tight control by the airport's ATC staff. Fortunately, Luton's taxiway problem is well known by pilots, and they all cooperate with each other and ATC to assist in the smooth running. Luton has planning permission, and is to build a parallel taxiway along with new aircraft stands, an improved apron area as well as a new control tower.

Runways

Luton has three runways. In order of size, they are: main, 08/26, at 7,087 feet (2,160 metres) long, by 150 feet (45 metres) wide. It has ILS

Luton Airport (*reproduced by kind permission of Luton Airport plc*)

at both ends. 18/36 is a grass runway 2,244 feet (683 metres) long by 82 feet (25 metres) wide. There is no ILS for this runway. The smallest runway, 06/24, again a grass runway is 1,296 feet (395 metres) long by 59 feet (18 metres) wide. There is no ILS for this runway either.

Spectator Facilities

You can't really get much better facilities for plane spotting than a purpose-made building! Luton provides a spectator area in a building near to the runway, across the taxiway from the airport's fire station. It has its own car park, and within the actual building there is a cafeteria, bar, toilets, telephones and an Airshop, selling aviation-related goods. Telephone the Information Desk on 0582 405100, Extension 212 for further information.

Getting There

By road, the M1, A1M, M25 motorways all provide access, with the relevant exit junctions well signposted. British Rail Luton links with St. Pancras and Kings Cross in London – journey time around 25 minutes. And of course the Inter-City 125s connect Luton with the rest of the country. Coach services link Luton to London, and many cities provide direct coach access to the airport. There is ample car parking at Luton; and disabled spotters can park free of charge (up to 12 hours) in the spectators car park by displaying their Orange Badge.

Part 3
Air Traffic Control

INTRODUCTION TO AIR TRAFFIC CONTROL

Air Traffic Control is a beautifully simple operation, on the surface. To most air travellers it is simply 'something to do with the airport getting the flights away on time'. To the average man and woman on the street it is something 'to do with aeroplanes or airports'; but exactly what they couldn't, if pushed for an answer, say for certain. That's just how simple it is – the general public hardly notice it at all. It works, that's all that matters.

Yet, as with all things which appear simple at first sight, beneath the surface air traffic control is a very complex mixture made up of: state-of-the-art computer systems, high-tech radio, radar and radio-navigation aids, navigation satellites, 'motorways' in the air and, by far the single most vital part of the whole air traffic control system, the highly trained men and women who manage and control all the computers and machines, and make air traffic control work.

What Is Air Traffic Control?

Often it seems that with all sorts of aircraft flying in all directions at various heights and times, there can't really be any control over them, their pilots or where and when they're going, can there?

Let's see. We have small aeroplanes, hot air balloons, gliders, hang-gliders and microlights; even the odd airship or two. The pilots of such aircraft fly them as a hobby – for fun, or as a form of personal transport. Apart from friends, they don't usually carry fare-paying passengers. The pilot of such an aircraft, especially when flying for fun, doesn't want loads of rules and regulations spoiling his or her enjoyment.

And then we have flight BD201, the 0710 British Midland Airways scheduled service six days a week from East Midlands International Airport to Amsterdam. The aircraft is a British Aerospace BAe ATP – Advanced Turbo Prop – seating some sixty-eight passengers. This flight has to leave at a fixed time and arrive at Amsterdam on schedule. It is a 'big' aircraft with the safety of over seventy people to consider as well as the multimillion pound value of the aeroplane itself. Further, flight BD201 isn't the only aircraft flying to Amsterdam at around that time. Other countries want to fly there as well, and this busy Dutch city has its share of flights heading our way too.

The problem is, how do we allow the pilots of small aircraft, microlights, hot air balloons and airships etc. to have their fun while making certain that flight 201 leaves the airport on time. Flying in the direction it wants at a height which allows the BD201 ATP to travel at its best speed to maintain schedule and conserve fuel, keeping all those other aircraft which are travelling to, from, over, north-south-east and west of Amsterdam (or East Midlands) well clear of it for safety, and still allowing flight 201 to arrive exactly on time?

The answer, of course, is Air Traffic Control; almost always known by its initials 'ATC', air traffic control arranges things so that the pilots of light aircraft, balloons etc. have the space to 'do their thing', while commercial aircraft (those which carry fare-paying passengers or cargo) also have maximum protection from all other aircraft, so that at no time will either interfere with the other.

Controlled Airspace

ATC manages the requirements of different types of aircraft by keeping them apart. It does this by sectioning off parts of the sky, and only allowing authorised aircraft into those areas; what's known as Controlled Airspace. This is areas of sky which have special rules, and an aircraft may only enter this special airspace under certain rules and conditions. Before any aircraft may enter an area of controlled airspace it must ask for and be granted prior permission to do so from ATC.

The most obvious place for control of aircraft, and the only real area where you can actually see this aircraft management in action, is at an airport. There you will see aeroplanes taking-off and landing. At the airport there are aircraft descending to land, others climbing away after take-off, light aeroplanes, perhaps a local flying school, buzzing around the terminal perimeter, flights passing over the airport en route to other places, aircraft moving around the terminal's runway, taxiways and apron areas and then local air traffic within a few miles of the airport. All this movement has to be controlled so that pilots never end up staring angrily, or more likely, unbelievingly into each other's eyes half-way down the runway!

Diagram 9 shows the controlled airspace around an airport. The Special Rules Zone (SRZ), sometimes called a Control Zone, starts at ground level and goes up to around 2,000 feet (although this does vary from terminal to terminal), and extends outwards around 5 miles either end of the centrepoint of the runway. The SRZ protects aircraft on take-off and landing from any other aircraft within the special rules zone. All aircraft flying within the SRZ need ATC permission, will be identified and their positions made known to the ATC controller responsible for the operation of the airport's runway, who uses a mixture of airport radar and radio messages to keep informed. An SRZ is no place to go flying a kite!

Aircraft descending from cruise level to land at the airport, or climbing away after take-off will be above 2,000 feet at 10 miles to/from the terminal, therefore above the special rules zone. These aeroplanes need protecting from aircraft movements on the runway (and of course,

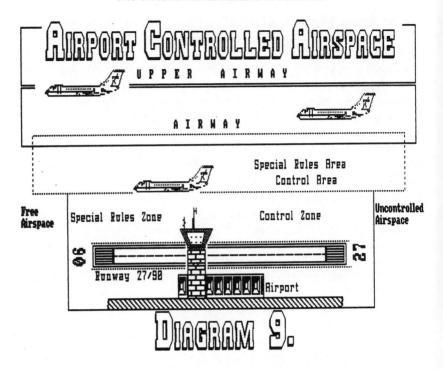

DIAGRAM 9.

vice-versa), but they don't need this cover all the way down to the ground – that's what the SRZ is for.

There is another controlled area known as the Special Rules Area (SRA), sometimes known as a Control Area (CA), which starts where the SRZ ends, around 2,000 feet above the ground, and goes up to around 4,000 feet which is approximately the base of the 'low-level airways' system. The upper limit of the SRA also varies greatly from airport to airport, and, although Diagram 9 shows a perfect symmetry to the controlled airspace around the airport this is often not the true case. Many airports have extensions to the SRA/SRZ producing 'bulges' and 'lumps' in their areas of controlled airspace, to allow for any special approach or departure routes.

The sky not labelled as controlled airspace in Diagram 9 is called 'Free Airspace'. This does not imply that there are *no* rules what-soever! What it does mean is that the rather stringent requirements for an aircraft to travel in controlled airspace do not apply within free airspace. However, in free – or more correctly, Uncontrolled Airspace – aircraft management is by Flight Information Region (FIR) of which there are two which cover the whole of the UK.

The London FIR is administered from the West Drayton Air Traffic

Control Centre – known as LATCC (you could try pronouncing it Lat-See) which is near Heathrow Airport in Middlesex. The Scottish FIR – SCATCC (try Skat-See) is administered from near Prestwick Airport. Briefly, Flight Information Regions provide flight data and services for pilots flying outside of controlled airspace.

As a working 'rule of thumb' private, light aircraft, hot air balloons, hang-gliders, airships and microlights tend to fly within uncontrolled airspace, enjoying the relative freedom and relaxation from strict control, while still having access to the services of Flight Information Regions. Commercial aircraft fly within controlled airspace. Which brings me nicely to the two main types of flying conditions for an aircraft when occupying either type of airspace.

Fly By Eye

If we take the case of a private, light aircraft flying in uncontrolled airspace first. The pilot of this aircraft is responsible for finding his way about. He or she (there are many female private and commercial pilots), is also responsible for keeping a look-out for any other aircraft in the immediate area, and for avoiding them if and when this becomes necessary. When an aircraft is flying in such conditions it is said to be flying Visual Flight Rules, abbreviated to VFR – spoken phonetically over the VHF airband radio as 'Victor-Fox-Romeo' – which usually gets shortened by pilot and ATCO alike to 'Victor-Fox'.

Visual Flight Rules (VFR)

Visual Flight Rules are just that: a set of regulations for all aircraft which are flying by pilot's eyesight in uncontrolled airspace. These rules are: between 3–25,000 feet the pilot must have a forward visibility of at least 5 miles. He/she must keep clear of cloud for a radius of 1 mile horizontally and must be at least 1,000 feet clear of any cloud above/below. It is the pilot's responsibility to keep clear of any other air traffic in the vicinity, so a sharp look-out must be kept at all times.

Below the lower limit of 3,000 feet still VFR, there are additional rules which are: the pilot must keep within sight of the ground at all times, and if flying at a speed of less than 140 knots, has to maintain an all-round clearance from cloud of at least 1 mile. If the indicated airspeed of the aircraft is faster than 140 knots, the all-round clearance from cloud extends to 3 miles. These regulations, or conditions are known as Visual Meteorological Conditions (VMC) spoken phonetically as 'Victor-Mike-Charlie' over airband radio, which again usually becomes truncated to 'Victor-Mike' by pilots.

So, an aircraft flying within uncontrolled airspace is flying Visual

Flight Rules – VFR – under Visual Meteorological Conditions – VMC. (VFR and VMC always go together.) The pilot is not under direct air traffic control, is responsible for his/her own navigation and for keeping clear of all other traffic; but does have access to the FIR services.

FIRs provide a country-wide Flight Information Service (FIS) which can be called upon by a VFR/VMC aircraft via VHF airband radio. The service provided concerns weather reports, airport information, whether there is any 'conflicting traffic' (other aircraft) in the immediate vicinity and general navigation information. The FIS also give crossing permissions where the aircraft needs to route across an airway. In practice, aircraft in uncontrolled airspace tend to navigate from airport to airport, and of course, they cannot enter controlled airspace at the airport without prior permission (which is usually granted where the aircraft are passing through).

This seems the ideal opportunity for me to introduce you to some 'Airband-Speak' – that's ATC messages over radio. At the relevant places I will give you a written transcript of a conversation between a pilot and an air traffic control officer. Firstly just as it comes over the radio; then again as a plain English translation. The messages both ways are real, actually recorded on-site at East Midlands International,

New Approach Control Room, Heathrow Airport (*reproduced by kind permission of the CAA*)

Manchester, Birmingham, Leeds/Bradford and Heathrow airports; Netherfield and other airfields.

To avoid any possible embarrassment in every case I've changed the aircraft's callsign to a fictitious one. What follows may be an eye opener to those of you familiar with the *Manual of Air Traffic Services*, or CAP 413, but then the reality is always different to the theory.

In this example PILOT refers to the person flying the aircraft, while APPROACH is the Approach Controller working from the control tower at the airport, who's keeping an electronic eye on aircraft heading for the airport, or wanting to transit airport controlled airspace. You'll soon get the hang of things. By the time you have finished reading this Handbook you'll be as fluent in airband-speak as any grizzled Boeing 747 captain with 20,000 hours flying time or I'll eat my imitation leather Biggles' flying helmet, jodhpurs and white silk scarf!

PILOT: 'Castledon Approach good morning. Golf-Foxtrot-Mike-Delta-Quebec.'

APPROACH: 'Golf-Foxtrot-Mike-Delta-Quebec – Castledon Approach. Good morning.'

PILOT: 'Golf-Foxtrot-Mike-Delta-Quebec is a Cessna 172 out of Tatenhill into Gamston. Just passing North abeam Burnaston heading zero-five-zero – two-three-zero-zero feet, one-two-zero Victor-Mike-Charlie. Request Flight Information Service and, er. . the Castledon QNH.'

APPROACH: 'Golf-Foxtrot-Mike-Delta-Quebec, roger. Maintain VFR. The East Midlands QNH is one-zero-one-eight and the Barnsley; one-zero-one-one.'

PILOT: 'One-zero-one-eight – one-zero-one-one, and we're squawking four-three-two-one. Golf-Delta-Quebec.'

APPROACH: 'That's a roger. The only traffic I'm er. . aware of, although it's intensive air activity to the north, and all the other units operating is er. . a similar type just er. . airborne from Tatenhill, flying at a last reported twelve-thousand feet, and other traffic; a Cessna 152 out to the north flying VFR.'

PILOT: 'Ah, roger. Copy the PA28 traffic, he's with us now and also the 152 traffic – yeah?'

APPROACH: 'Yeah.'

So, in plain English, this is what's happening. A light aircraft, (type Cessna 172) has taken off from Tatenhill aerodrome and is making for Gamston aerodrome near Retford flying under Visual Meteorological Conditions (VMC), which means it's flying by Visual Flight Rules (VFR).

Next follows a stream of data which the Approach Controller must have to enable her to arrange the air traffic in her zone safely. The aircraft's present position is just passing north of Burnaston in Derby-shire, steering a magnetic compass course of 50 degrees ('zero-five-zero') at an altitude of two thousand-three hundred feet.

The aircraft's present speed is one-hundred and twenty knots and is flying VMC. The pilot then finishes with a request for the airport 'QNH', QNH is the air pressure reading around the airport which aircraft flying in uncontrolled airspace, and aircraft below the 'Transi-tion Altitude' must set on their altimeter.

Approach confirms that he's received all this information from the pilot ('. . . roger. Maintain VFR . . .') and passes *both* the East Mid-lands QNH and the 'Barnsley' which is a standard air pressure reading when flying within airspace covered by the Barnsley area of the UK Altimeter Settings Chart.

The pilot confirms he's received this information by repeating it back to the controller and then adds that he's 'squawking four-three-two-one'. This is a code set on the Secondary Surveillance Radar trans-ponder in the aircraft, and we'll be looking at it in greater detail later on.

Finally, the Approach Controller passes on all information she has about any other aircraft within the pilot's immediate area, warning him of intensive air activity 'to the North' (of East Midlands airspace), and further telling the pilot that there's a similar aircraft nearby, and a Cessna 152 trainer north of his position. The pilot confirms that he can actually see the 'similar type', but then asks Approach to confirm the presence of the Cessna 152 ('. . . also the 152, yeah?')

From this long-winded translation of the brief, snappy Radio Tele-phony (R/T) exchange between the airport control tower and a pilot, you can see the beauty of airband-speak! It really does save an awful lot of time. Don't worry about future R/T translations; I'll just be giving the parts which may not be too clear. Meanwhile; back at our aircraft flying in uncontrolled airspace VFR.

'Ah!' I hear you say. 'But what if the aircraft cannot meet the VFR/VMC conditions. What if he can't see 5 miles, what if he flies into thick cloud. And most of all, what happens at night?' Good questions.

Well, if the pilot cannot meet VFR/VMC requirements, then aviation law states that he or she must then be on Instrument Flight Rules (IFR), under Instrument Meteorological Conditions (IMC). 'India-Fox-Romeo' and 'India-Mike-Charlie' respectively, over the airband radio. And that's a whole new game, and the going now starts to get a little tough, especially for the private pilot!

Instrument Flight Rules (IFR)

Just like the *Rules* part of Visual Flight Rules, there are regulations for Instrument Flight Rules. These are: the aircraft must have certain items of radio and radar equipment on-board as specified by the Civil Aviation Authority (CAA). We'll be seeing what these are later on. The pilot of the aircraft flying under IFR must be qualified to do so. This in practice means that apart from the basic Private Pilot's Licence (PPL) he or she must have an Instrument Rating. Commercial pilots usually have to obtain an Instrument Rating as part of their training anyway.

So, an aircraft flying within controlled airspace must be on Instrument Flight Rules under Instrument Meteorological Conditions, therefore *all* aircraft within controlled airspace are flying IFR by definition.

Instruments by the way, are usually meters, pointers, digital scales and dials etc. in the cockpit which tell the pilot everything he/she needs to know about the current flying state of the aircraft. Such as how fast, in what direction and at what height is the aeroplane travelling, where the aircraft is, whether it's climbing or descending; even whether the aircraft is flying horizontally, or maybe tilted over to one side or the other.

The Instrument Rating is a test where pilots have to demonstrate to an examiner that they can fly the aircraft purely on instruments alone, without reference to the ground, or, more importantly, without sight of a local horizon. It's mainly done for real, in a flying aircraft, with the pilot having to wear a specially darkened hood which restricts his view to the inside of the cockpit and instrument panel only, simulating things as they would appear in bad weather or darkness. Increasingly, flight simulators are often used these days for instrument rating examinations.

An aircraft may be either VFR under Visual Meteorological Conditions, or Instrument Flight Rules under IMC. The aircraft *must* be either one or the other – if not VFR then IFR, if not IFR then VFR.

'Victor-Fox-Romeo' and 'Victor-Mike-Charlie' may often be heard by listeners on the VHF airband, although usually abbreviated by pilots to 'Victor-Fox' or 'Victor-Mike'. However, IFR/IMC isn't usually heard much, if at all. As practically all commercial flying takes place within controlled airspace, IFR/IMC is taken for granted.

One final point about VFR and IFR. Under Visual Flight Rules the pilot is responsible for keeping clear of all other aircraft. When flying on Instrument Flight Rules the responsibility for keeping clear of any conflicting traffic passes from the pilot of the aircraft directly to air traffic control.

Summary

We've seen the need for ATC, I've told you a bit about what air traffic control does and we've discussed controlled airspace around the airport. To move on. The 'Control' aspect of air traffic control, and the only part we, as aviation enthusiasts, can really experience at first hand, consists of verbal instructions (which have the weight of civil law behind them) given out by a properly licensed Air Traffic Control Officer (ATCO) to the pilot of an aircraft. Very High Frequency (VHF) radio is the means by which these instructions are delivered to the pilot, and of course, we can pick up these messages, bearing in mind the

Gatwick Airport Control Tower (*reproduced by kind permission of the CAA*)

'clarification' of the law regarding the reception of airband radio signals I related in the introduction.

ATC is responsible for the SRZ/SRAs at the airports, and of course *all* aircraft movement (and other vehicles too). The place where these people work, and the centre of airport ATC is the terminal's Control Tower, and that's where we're off to next.

AIR TRAFFIC CONTROL AT THE AIRPORT

We now know that the control aspect of ATC takes the form of verbal instructions from a duly licensed Air Traffic Control Officer (ATCO). We can both see and hear this part of ATC at work at an aerodrome by observing, and listening on our airband receivers. Most airport ATCOs work within the Control Tower, easily the most recognizable building at an airport.

The Control Tower

Control towers are very tall structures usually the highest building at the aerodrome. Right at the very top of the tower can be seen various

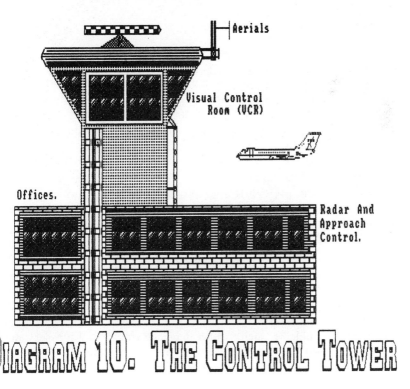

DIAGRAM 10. THE CONTROL TOWER

radio aerials. Sometimes there will be a ASMI (Aerodrome Surface Movement Indicator) radar antenna rotating quickly, while others may have a non-rotating plastic bulge (radome) housing the ASMI radar array. Smaller airports don't usually have any ASMI radar at all.

Below the radio aerials on the roof there is a room which has large glass windows usually running right around the building. Although at some control towers these windows only face 'Airside'; which means that part of the airport which has to do with the terminal's taxiways, ramp or stands, runway and aprons – the *manoeuvering* area. Unless you're actually boarding or getting off an aircraft, the general public are not allowed airside.

Diagram 10 is a drawing of a typical aerodrome control tower to be found at many regional airports around the UK. The glass-walled room at the top is known as the Visual Control Room (VCR). Air traffic control officers who work in the VCR need an all-round clear view of the airport's manoeuvering area; that's why the control tower building is so tall. They need to keep a careful eye on aircraft movements around the airport and visually confirm that their instructions have been carried out.

Airport Air Traffic Control Officers

Time to meet the people. If you visit the same airport on a regular basis you quickly begin to recognize voices, and their owner's special way of doing things. The first person we'll get to know via our airband receivers is 'Tower'. This is the person in charge of the airport's runway. Tower says when an aircraft may enter the runway, prepare for, and then take-off. Similarly, Tower's permission has to be received before an aircraft may land. Tower uses VHF radio to send control instructions to a pilot, and binoculars to see what's happening around the manoeuvering area.

The Ground Movement Controller (GMC) – 'Ground' over radio – does exactly that. He controls all movement of vehicles on the ground except on the actual runway itself, which is Tower's responsibility. This includes aircraft at the parking stands, where passengers board the aeroplanes, along the taxiways, where aircraft manoeuvre around the airport, right up to the runway holding point – which is a stop position just short of the actual runway. At the holding point 'Ground' passes control of the aircraft over to 'Tower'. As well as using VHF airband radio to talk to the pilots, Ground also makes use of Ultra High Frequency (UHF) radio to keep in contact with airport service and maintenance vehicles, such as tugs, baggage trains, fuel bowsers etc.

Ground also has responsibility for the airside lighting. He has to control the many lamps and illumination patterns of the runway,

Visual Control Room, Gatwick Airport Control Tower (*reproduced by kind permission of the CAA*)

taxiways and apron areas. These lights are often very complicated and form part of the airport's Instrument Landing System (ILS) category rating. There's not a lot of point in landing an aircraft in zero visibility if Ground can't get it off the runway and over to the ramp or stands because the pilot can't see a thing!

Below the Visual Control Room is 'Approach Control', usually shortened to just 'Approach'. They normally work from a radar screen, in a specially darkened room, keeping track of incoming and outgoing aircraft positions using a Radar Visual Display Unit (RVDU), and talking to the pilots on VHF airband radio.

Approach Control takes over responsibility for an incoming flight from the En-route controller. Sometimes, working alongside 'Approach' in approach control there is a Radar Controller, known as 'Radar', who keeps track of aircraft movements in the Special Rules Area (Control Area), separating them from aircraft over-flying, descending to land, or climbing-out after take-off.

What's In A Name

Each controller who works in the tower – Ground, Approach, Radar and Tower – has an individual radio frequency. And, as airport ATC staff are usually 'named' after the job they do, they're called over air-band radio by this name. Thus the pilot of an incoming aircraft wanting permission to land will call Tower, and get his or her approval. Once safely down the pilot will be advised to contact Ground.

And that is basically the airport control tower and the people who work in it. Of course, control towers vary from aerodrome to aerodrome, as do the number of staff who work in them. At Heathrow Airport, which has *two* runways, there are separate Tower controllers for arrivals and departures, a Ground Movement Planner (GMP) often called 'Delivery', a Ground Movement Controller (GMC) and various assistants, and training ATCOs. Certainly a very crowded visual control room.

Smaller terminals may have no Radar Controller, other aerodromes may have no Ground Movement Controller, with Tower performing this function. Although almost all airports have at least two ATCOs in the control tower: Aerodrome and Approach Control. At an airfield there'll just be the one person who has to do everything. Two main things happen at an airport: aircraft take-off and aircraft land. On the runway. Usually! Let's now see how departures and arrivals are handled by airport ATC.

Departures

With a light aircraft planning to fly in uncontrolled airspace, take-off from an airport is a fairly straightforward procedure. The pilot will ask for 'taxi' – permission to move onto the taxiway and head for the runway. Tower will tell the light aircraft pilot to 'Line Up' (move onto the runway and prepare for, *but do not* take-off, until further clearance). When everything's OK Tower clears the pilot for take-off. Prior to the aircraft actually entering the runway only the word 'Departure' is used, take-off being reserved for just that purpose only.

However, for a commercial aircraft the procedure is not so simple. One of the conditions for IFR/IMC flights is that prior permission to enter controlled airspace must be gained before entry. Commercial aircraft do this by filing a Flight Plan with the relevant Air Traffic Control Centre (ATCC), which in the UK means either SCATCC or LATCC.

Flight Plans

What the flight plan does is to inform the ATCC of the intentions of the airline company, details such as the type of aircraft, what terminal it will leave from, at what time, where it's going, what route, altitude and speed are preferred, and what time it will arrive at its destination.

This may seem an awful lot to ask, but with aircraft flying to other countries there's more than just United Kingdom controlled airspace to consider. At the ATCC flight plans are studied, and, as far as is possible, the airline company's requirements are met.

The ATCC will confirm the flight plan, check with other countries that it can accept the flight at that time, request permission for the flight to transit their controlled airspace, and then enter all the details in a computer. Finally, the ATCC will issue the flight with an Approved Departure Time (ADT). Airband listeners often hear pilots discussing 'Slots', which are in effect the ADT.

Of course, the airline companies don't have to keep on bothering the airport's flight scheduling committee, or LATCC every time they want to fly somewhere. Most flights are scheduled services, and as such the flight plans remain in the ATC computer until such time as that particular scheduled service is cancelled.

Flight Progress Strips

About an hour before the flight is due for take-off (Approved Departure Time), the ATCC activates the flight plan and passes the flight details over the telephone landline, using telex, to the departure airport. At the departure airport a Flight Progress Strip (FPS) is printed automatically onto a piece of cardboard from the information supplied by the ATCC. The strip is then placed inside a plastic sleeve and slotted into the pending departures rack on the desk of the Ground Movement Planner in the control tower.

This strip of paper becomes a continuously updated life history of the flight. It will exist for as long as the flight lasts, and will be passed from country to country, from ATCO to ATCO until the aircraft safely lands at its destination. ATC decisions affecting the flight will be written on the FPS, and if we follow this air traffic control version of the 'relay baton' we can get to know the airport ATC staff much better.

Fastjet Eight-Zero!

Fastjet Eight-Zero is an imaginary Boeing 747-400 belonging to Flying Fox Airlines, departing London Heathrow for JFK – Kennedy Airport in New York. This is a scheduled service, so LATCC has its details inside its computer. Approved Departure (slot) time is 1430. North Atlantic flights heading west are scheduled around the same time – early afternoon, giving an early evening arrival. (New York is five hours behind GMT.) Eastbound crossings usually take-off in the evenings, giving an early morning arrival this side of the Atlantic. This system helps to control the number of flights crossing the North Atlantic

Ocean, providing a measure of separation in what can be tremendously busy airspace.

At 1330 the crew of Fastjet Eight-Zero reported for duty, checked the company notice board, picked up departure, en-route and arrival weather information, and boarded the aircraft for pre-take-off checks. At the same time as the crew reported for duty, LATCC activated Fastjet Eight-Zero's flight plan.

Ground Movement Planner – GMP

In the tower, Heathrow Delivery, the Ground Movement Planner (GMP) checks his rack for pending departures. As Fastjet Eight-Zero's ADT moves nearer, he expects a call on the Delivery frequency. One of his jobs is to confirm the aircraft's flight plan and issue Fastjet Eight-Zero with route clearance – assuming there aren't any problems, of course. The original flight plan may have been filed many months ago, so any problems since then, such as navigation beacons out of commission, airport construction work, or anything else which could affect the aircraft's original plan, has to be double checked. Knowing that he can't proceed until he's received flight plan clearance, the captain of Fastjet Eight-Zero doesn't start the aircraft's engines until he has GMP's permission. Aviation fuel costs far too much to burn idly, whilst waiting for ATC clearance.

PILOT: 'Heathrow Delivery – Fastjet Eight-Zero at Lima two-two with Bravo. Good afternoon.'

Trans: Aircraft, whose R/T callsign is 'Fastjet Eight-Zero', currently parked at stand L22 has received the latest Automatic Terminal Information Service (ATIS) weather and terminal information. It is implicit in the call to 'Delivery' that Fastjet Eight-Zero requires route clearance as well.

GMP: 'Fastjet Eight-Zero, Heathrow Delivery. Good afternoon. Cleared start for Kennedy with a Brecon Golf-one departure. Squawk five-three-four-one, please.'
PILOT: 'Fastjet Eight-Zero has start. Clear JFK with a Brecon Golf-one. Squawk five-three-four-one. Thanks.'
GMP: 'Correct. One-two-one decimal niner next, for pushback.'
PILOT: 'One-two-one decimal niner. Bye.'
GMP: 'Bye.'

Trans: Fastjet Eight-Zero has route clearance, permission to start engines and instructions to continue with the Ground Movement Controller on a frequency of 121.900mHz. Aircraft park 'nose-in' at the stands, and passengers board via a covered walkway extending from the

Departures lounge to the aircraft's front doors. The aeroplane cannot use its own engines to reverse away from the stand, therefore an airport tug will quite literally push the aircraft backwards away from the stand, and position it facing a taxiway entry point. Fastjet Eight- Zero's Flight Progress Strip is marked by Delivery and passed on to GMC.

Take-Off

DEPARTURES: 'Fastjet Eight-Zero, after the seven-three-seven line-up; two-seven right.'

PILOT: 'After the seven-three-seven line-up and hold. Fastjet Eight-Zero.'

DEPARTURES: 'Fastjet Eight-Zero cleared take-off two seven right. Wind two- two-zero at eight.'

PILOT: 'Clear take-off. Fastjet Eight-Zero.'

Fastjet Eight-Zero hurtles down the runway and up into the air. There's one final message from the Air-'D' controller.

DEPARTURES: 'Fastjet Eight-Zero airborne at three-three. One-two-eight decimal niner, London next. Goodbye.'

PILOT: 'One-two-eight decimal niner. Thanks and good bye.'

Control of Fastjet Eight-Zero now passes directly to the London Air Traffic Control Centre (LATCC) at West Drayton. The Flight Progress Strip, complete with the new information supplied by 'Delivery, Ground and Air-'D'' passes to LATCC via teleprinter, and the sector controller there is expecting Fastjet Eight-Zero's call at any time.

And that is take-off for an IFR/IMC flight at London Heathrow. At regional airports the procedure is identical, the only variation will be in the number of ATCOs dealing with the flight. For example, at East Midlands, there's no Delivery (Ground Movement Planner), GMC or Air-'D'. Clearance, pushback and taxi are dealt with by Tower. After take-off control is passed to 'Approach' until the hand-over to En-route ATC.

Arrivals

En-route ATC, which takes care of aircraft flying in controlled airspace along the airways system between airports, will pass management of the arriving aircraft over to the airport Approach Controller at an agreed location. En-route Control descends the aircraft from cruise level, gives the pilot a radar heading to steer, tells him to contact Approach, and then relinquishes control.

The hand-over usually takes place around a beacon near to the airport, such as a Non-Directional Beacon (NDB). It's difficult for an airband listener to know where this hand-over occurs because it is pre-arranged between the En-route and Approach controllers over the telephone landline. A Flight Progress Strip will be made up at the airport ready for the incoming aircraft.

As much as possible, airports try for continuous descent, straight-in approaches; where the aircraft simply enjoys a gradual loss of height terminating with a gentle bump onto the airport's runway, thereby saving a lot of time and fuel. At regional airports, which are in the main less busy than the BAA terminals, this is often achieved. However, airports in the London Terminal Control Area (TMA) very rarely find themselves able to do this, and have to resort to special measures which I'll discuss in a while. First I'll deal with arrivals at a regional airport, which are quite straightforward.

PILOT: 'Castledon Approach – Midland Nine-Zero-Zero turning for the Echo-Mike-Echo. Cleared to six-zero.'

Trans: British Midland Airways flight Midland 900 (a DC9-15) is heading for the East Midland Non-Directional Beacon; callsign EME, and has been cleared down to 6,000 feet by En-route ATC.

APPROACH: 'Thanks Midland Nine-Zero-Zero. Radar to ILS runway two-seven, the weather when ready . . .'
PILOT: 'Go ahead.'
APPROACH: 'Surface wind is one-niner-zero, fifteen knots. Twenty-five kilometers three oktas. Two-fife-zero-zero - six oktas four-fife-zero-zero feet. Temperature two-zero, dew point one-three. QNH is one-zero-one-eight. Caution, the PAPIs are unserviceable – they will be so for the next ten minutes.'
PILOT: 'OK - one-zero-one-eight - PAPIs out, and we copied the rest. Nine-Zero-Zero.'
APPROACH: 'Midland Nine-Zero-Zero on one-zero-one-eight milli-bars descend three thousand feet.'
PILOT: 'Three thousand on one-zero-one-eight. Nine-Zero-Zero.'
APPROACH: 'Midland Nine-Zero-Zero, turn left heading three-six-zero base-leg. Descend two-thousand feet.'
PILOT: 'Two-thousand – left three-sixty base. Midland Nine-Zero-Zero.'
APPROACH: 'Nine-Zero-Zero report established.'
PILOT: 'Midland Nine-Zero-Zero, established.'

Trans: Flight Midland Nine-Zero-Zero has acquired the ILS Local-iser *and* the Glide Slope signals and is correctly lined up for landing.

APPROACH: 'Midland Nine-Zero-Zero cleared visual approach. The circuit is active, I think you're number one. Call Tower now – one-two-four decimal zero.'

PILOT: 'OK for visual. One-two-four zero. Bye bye.'

APPROACH: 'Bye.'

PILOT: 'Ah Midland Nine-Zero-Zero turning final two-seven.'

TOWER: 'Midland Nine-Zero-Zero, good morning. Continue approach – number 1.'

PILOT: 'Nine-Zero-Zero.'

TOWER: 'Nine-Zero-Zero clear to land two-seven. The wind – two-one-zero, seventeen knots.'

PILOT: 'Clear to land two-seven. Midland Nine-Zero-Zero.'

GOLF-PAPA: 'Golf-papa has the DC9 in site.'

TOWER: 'Golf-Papa, Roger. Report final. Number 2. Caution – wake turbulence.'

GOLF-PAPA: 'Report final, number 2 er. . the caution's copied. Golf-Papa.'

TOWER: 'Midland Nine-Zero-Zero, be advised, the PAPIs are now serviceable.'

PILOT: 'Got it, thank you.'

TOWER: 'Nine-Zero-Zero – vacate next-left. Stand number seven.'

PILOT: 'Left and seven. Nine-Zero-Zero.'

GOLF-PAPA: 'Golf-Papa on final.'

TOWER: 'Golf-Papa, roger. Clear to land, two-seven. Wind two-two-five at ten.'

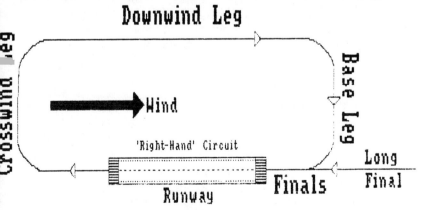

DIAGRAM 11. AIRPORT CIRCUIT.

Downwind Leg

Crosswind Leg

Wind

Base Leg

'Right-Hand' Circuit

Long Final

Runway

Finals

The 'Dead' Side.

GOLF-PAPA: 'Ah. roger tower. Clear to land – two-seven. Thanks.'
TOWER: 'My pleasure.'

Airport Circuit

When 'Midland Nine-Zero-Zero' reported 'Established' on the ILS system, Tower passed a warning that the circuit was active. At aerodromes where a lot of light aircraft are flown – such as flying schools, which are often based at regional airports, for airfields outside controlled airspace, and for VFR pilots – a circular traffic pattern around the airport perimeter is set up (see Diagram 11).

The circuit may be either right-hand or left. On a right-hand circuit all turns will be right turns and vice-versa. A total of four 90 degree right or left turns are made, with each turn given a name: Crosswind, Downwind, Base and Final. Control is much the same whether an airport or airfield. The pilot has to report his position on the circuit, and receive the necessary permission for take-off and landing.

Standard Instrument Departures – SID

To maximise runway potential and to route aircraft taking-off away from heavily populated residential areas, busy airports have Standard Instrument Departure routes – SIDs. These departure plans enable a much higher traffic density to be maintained as they channel aircraft departing on similar routes along standard pathways, which cuts down enormously on the amount of radio telephony messages between ATC and the pilots, freeing the controllers for much more productive work.

SIDs consist of courses to steer, navigation beacons to head for and certain altitude limitations to observe. Jet aircraft are at their noisiest on take-off, so airport authorities lay down Noise Abatement procedures to alleviate the local problem. The illustration on the opposite page shows an SID chart for London Heathrow Airport.

Standard Terminal Arrival Routes

Similar to SIDs are Standard Terminal Arrival Routes (STAR), which perform much the same job as an SID but in reverse. Heathrow Airport, the busiest air terminal in the world has four entry points each marked with a VOR/DME beacon . There is a STAR for each of these beacons, two of which are located to the north of Heathrow, and two to the south. These beacons are Bovingdon and Lambourne to the north, Ockham and Biggin to the south. All aircraft heading for Heathrow will be delivered to one of these VORs by En-route ATC and then handed-over to Heathrow Approach for landing sequencing.

(HEATHROW) LONDON
SOUTHAMPTON SID

EGLL

| Trans alt **6000** | | | G7 | L9 |

1. Initial climb: Ahead to 580. **2.** En-route cruising level will be given by LONDON Control after take-off. **3.** Callsign for RTF frequency use when instructed after take-off 'LONDON Control'. **4.** Max 250kt IAS below FL100 unless otherwise authorised. **5.** For Noise Measurement Sites, see C1.

EFF 20 SEP 90

NOT TO SCALE

AVERAGE TRACK MILEAGE TO SAM
SAM 2F/2G 48
SAM 2H 49
SAM 2J/2K 53

SAM 040R

SAM 2F,2G

LON 12d above **3000**

LON 113·6 LON 1·3d

Abm WOD LON 15d — Woodley 'WOD' 352

above **4000**

LON 7d 260° 273° 278° 129°

LON 13d LON 260R

LON 2d LON 5d

OCK 046R

LON 119R

LON 129R

SAM 2F:2G:2H

SAM 2H

SAM 27d above **5500**

226°

OCK 2d above **3000**

SAM 2J:2K

SAM 24d at **6000**

220° 25nm SAM 052R

OCK 3d above **4000**

Ockham OCK 115·3

OCK 19d 258°

OCK 7d above **5000**

OCK 11d at **6000**

232°

| 2₂ | 2₃ |
| 2₁ | 2₃ |

SSA 25nm

SOUTHAMPTON SAM 113·35
N50 57·3
W001 20·6

SID	R/W	ROUTEING (including Min Noise Routeing)	ALTITUDES
SAM 2F 123.9	27R	Ahead to intercept LON 260R to LON 7d then right on Tr273M ('WOD' 273M). At LON 13d left onto Tr220M (SAM 040R) to SAM.	LON 12d above 3000 ABM WOD/LON 15d above 4000 SAM 27d above 5500 SAM 24d at 6000
SAM 2G 123.9	27L	Ahead to intercept LON 260R to LON 7d then right on Tr273M ('WOD' 273M). At LON 13d left onto Tr220M (SAM 040R) to SAM.	
SAM 2H 123.9	23	At LON 2d right onto Tr278M ('WOD' 278M). At LON 13d left onto Tr220M (SAM 040R) to SAM.	
SAM 2J 123.9	09R	Right to intercept LON 129R to LON 5d then right on Tr226M (OCK 046R). At OCK 2d right on OCK 258R to OCK 19d then left on Tr232M (SAM 052R) to SAM.	OCK 2d above 3000 OCK 3d above 4000 OCK 7d above 5000 OCK 11d at 6000
SAM 2K 123.9	09L	At LON 119R/1.3d right to intercept LON 129R to LON 5d then right on Tr226M (OCK 046R). At OCK 2d right to intercept OCK 258R to OCK 19d then left on Tr232M (SAM 052R) to SAM.	

Revision: Notes

BRITISH AIRWAYS AERAD

Arrivals chart, Heathrow Airport (*reproduced by kind permission of the British Airways Aerad*)

Approach Hold Procedures

Some airports, such as Gatwick, Heathrow and Manchester are very busy places. Heathrow has an aircraft movement around every minute or so at peak times. Dealing with Heathrow for the moment; although arrivals are via the four VOR beacons, only one runway is available for landings, albeit all the time, unlike Gatwick which has to sequence aircraft landing with those wishing to take-off. The Air Arrivals Controllers at Heathrow sequence aircraft away from the VOR beacons and arrange them in a neat and orderly queue ready for final approach, with an aircraft landing every four to five minutes or so.

But, at times more aircraft will arrive at the Heathrow entry points than Air Arrivals can cope with, which presents them with a problem. An aeroplane cannot 'hover' on a VOR until the way is clear for landing; the only things it may do are to slow down slightly, or to fly around in circles until the final approach can be made. When this situation arises, Heathrow Approach start to use the 'Hold' procedure.

The Stack

When the Hold procedure is being used, aircraft are 'stacked' one above the other at 1,000 feet intervals, and have to fly a race-track pattern around the VOR beacon. The first aircraft to arrive will be descended to 7,000 feet, and begin to circle the beacon, flying along a radial of the VOR for a minute, making a right-handed turn of 90 degrees and flying on for another minute, until a complete circuit of the beacon has been completed.

If instructions for leaving the stack still haven't been received, then the aircraft will begin another circuit. Aircraft have been known to orbit the VORs for half-an-hour or so! The next aircraft to arrive at the same beacon will be descended to 8,000 feet and begin its circuit. Aircraft continue to arrive, and are 'stacked' at 1,000 feet intervals, starting at 7,000 feet – the bottom of the stack – and working up to the maximum stack height of 13,000 feet.

As each aircraft is put into the stack, Approach Control marks its Flight Progress Strip with a 'H' for hold, and the time of arrival at the VOR. Apart from emergencies, aircraft are cleared from the holding stack in the same order they arrived – first in, first out. As each aeroplane is cleared from the bottom of the holding pattern to start its final approach, the aircraft above are cleared down to the next lower level.

The process continues while more aircraft arrive than can be brought straight in for landing. Aeroplanes arrive and are put into the top of the stack while those who have been there longest are cleared from the

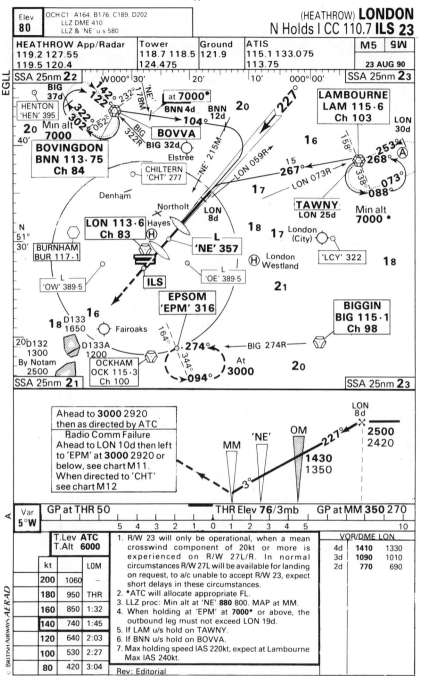

SID chart, London Heathrow Airport (*reproduced by kind permission of the British Airways Aerad*)

bottom for final approach and landing. Eventually things quieten down and the Air Arrivals Controller can once again route aircraft from the entrypoint VOR beacons straight in for finals.

EN-ROUTE AIR TRAFFIC CONTROL

Airways

Airways are literally motorways in three dimensions up in the skies. They are the major routes for commercial aircraft between air terminals in Britain and Europe.

Airways are corridors of controlled airspace ten miles wide. They start at an average height of around 4,000 feet and extend upwards to 24,500 feet, which is the base of Upper Airspace in the UK. Airways are 'named' with a letter and number. They used to be called by quasi romantic names, such as Blue 4, Amber 25 and Red 3; but now they've been redesignated with the ICAO phonetic alphabet, Bravo 4, Alpha 25 and Romeo 3 (see Diagram 12).

I've already explained the rules of entry into controlled airspace, but briefly, the aircraft must fly IFR and carry a certain minimum level of radionavigation equipment. Aircraft flying west will fly at EVEN thousands of feet within the airway while eastbound fly at ODD thousands. The centre of each airway is marked with either a VHF

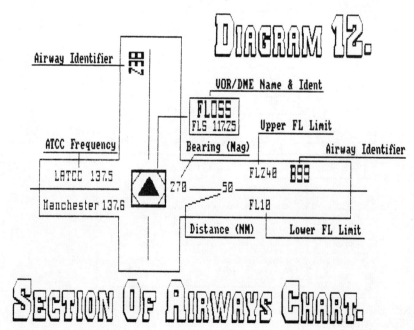

DIAGRAM 12.

Airway Identifier

VOR/DME Name & Ident

FLOSS
FLS 117.25   Upper FL Limit

ATCC Frequency   Bearing (Mag)   Airway Identifier

LATCC 137.5   270 — 50   FLZ40 B99

Manchester 137.6   FL10

Distance (NM)   Lower FL Limit

SECTION OF AIRWAYS CHART.

Omni-Range (VOR) navigation beacon, or an NDB, as are all airway junctions.

Along the length of the airways are various standard and compulsory reporting points, where a pilot must call the relevant Airways Air Traffic Control Centre (LATCC, SCATCC or the Manchester sub-centre) and state the location and altitude of the aeroplane. Aircraft fly along the airways by navigating from VOR beacon to beacon, following a particular radial. VHF Omni-Range beacons are fully explained in the ATC Navigation Aids section (see Diagram 13).

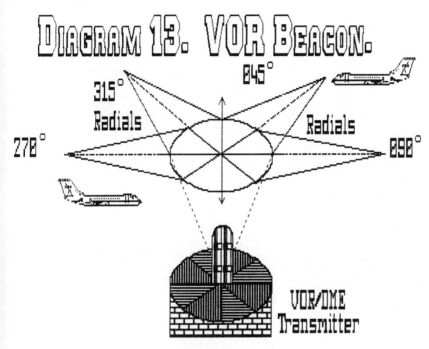

London and Scottish Air Traffic Control Centres

LATCC, London ATCC and SCATCC, Scottish ATCC, together with the ATC sub-centre at Manchester (which looks after aircraft in the Manchester TMA below 15,500 feet) manage En-route ATC between them. LATCC's responsibility ends at latitude 55 degrees North, roughly along the England/Scotland border, where SCATCC takes over. Both ATCCs also manage the Terminal Manoeuvering (Control) Areas (TMAs) which are areas of controlled airspace around busy airports. The London TMA covers Heathrow, Gatwick, Stansted, and Luton airports, and exists to protect aircraft ascending/descending from airways onto the runways.

En-route ATC has remote radio transmitters and receivers, together

DIAGRAM 14.

CAA REMOTE RADAR SITES.

1. Stornoway
2. Tiree
3. Lowther Hill
4. Great Dun Fell
5. Claxby
6. Clee Hill
7. Debden
8. Heathrow
9. Ash
10. Pease Pottage
11. Burrington
12. Ventnor (IOW)
13. Mount Gabriel

PART ONE.

PART TWO.

CAA REMOTE RADIO RELAY SITES.

1. Craigowl
2. Rhu
3. Prestwick
4. Lowther Hill
5. Boulmer
6. Great Dun Fell
7. Snaefell (IOM)
8. Preston
9. Claxby
10. Grantham

11. Daventry
12. Trimmingham
13. Chedburgh
14. Greenford
15. Heathrow
16. Warlingham
17. Pease Pottage
18. Burrington
19. Davidstowe
20. Ventnor (IOW)

with radar units scattered around the country, all of which are linked by telephone datalines back to the ATCC (see Diagram 14). Because of the huge area covered by LATCC, the country is divided into sectors, each of which has its own controllers, and VHF radio frequencies.

The main LATCC sectors are: Irish Sea, Strumble, Cardiff, along the West coast. Pole Hill in the North, Bristol in the West and Daventry covering the Midlands. Clacton, covering the East coast and Hurn/ Seaford, Dover/Lydd along the South coast. The London TMA is also divided into four sectors; North East and West, South East and West, again each with its own controllers and frequencies.

During the day these sectors are quite busy, and most of the En-route ATC frequencies (Airways Frequencies) will be in use. However, at night, when air traffic diminishes, sectors will be 'stood down' and often combine into several much larger areas controlled by one or two ATCOs using a different airways frequency than is normally used for that particular sector.

So if a busy airways frequency you like to monitor disappears at night you now know why! As the day shift arrive, the various sectors will once again be re-activated and return to their usual frequency allocations. There is a list of low-level and high-level airways together with their controlling ATCCs and frequencies in the Radiodatabase section.

Upper Airways

Low-level airways finish at a height of 24,500 feet. At this altitude, high-level airways take over, extending upwards from the base level of 24,500 feet to around 60,000 feet. They virtually follow the paths of the airways beneath them, and share the same names prefixed by the word Upper such as Upper-Bravo 4 and Upper Alpha 25. Upper airways are more loosely defined than the lower airways, and are in fact Special Rules Areas.

Unlike the low-level airways, where pilots navigate from beacon to beacon, following the path of the airway, aircraft flying within upper airways are usually allowed to fly directly towards VOR beacons, rather than slavishly follow the path of the lower route. This represents a large saving in fuel, time and the amount of R/T traffic between the aircraft and the En-route Controller.

Airspace below 24,500 feet is covered by either the London or Scottish Flight Information Regions. Upper airspace comes under the umbrella of the Upper Flight Information Regions (UIR) again administered by either Scotland or London. Oceanic Link Routes allow a more direct approach to oceanic entry points from upper airspace, with the Concordes having their own Supersonic Link Routes (SL route).

Upper airways are not just restricted to UK airspace. For example, airway Upper-Bravo 1. This high-level airway starts over North Africa, then follows the path Greece, Yugoslavia, Austria, Germany, arriving on the Dutch coast at Amsterdam. From the Netherlands, UB1 crosses the North Sea, routing via the Otteringham VOR near Hull, across central England to the Wirral on the Western coast. From Merseyside, Upper Bravo 1 crosses the Irish Sea, over Dublin and ends at County Mayo on Ireland's Western coastline.

The Altimeter

If a pilot is to avoid flying her aircraft into the ground, or through a mountain, then she must know the height of her aircraft above the surface. The standard instrument which measures an aircraft's height above ground is the altimeter. There are two versions of this instrument, one works by radio and the other by air pressure. The radio altimeter is only used in certain circumstances. Due to its accuracy it cannot be used for normal flight. When an aircraft's autopilots are engaged, the altimeter is also linked so that not only is correct course maintained but height as well.

If the radio altimeter were used for this, then the aircraft would be continuously rising and falling as the signal from the radio altimeter transponder followed the contours of the ground beneath it! Radio altimeters are used only on final approach to an airport by certain aircraft types.

The pressure altimeter works like a barometer by measuring atmospheric air pressure. A tube on the front of the aircraft's fuselage (the Pitot tube) collects air and passes it into the casing of the altimeter where a special capsule expands and contracts according to the pressure acting upon it. The movement of this tube is picked up by mechanical linkages and moves a pointer across the dial of the altimeter on the flight deck. No problems so far.

But, air pressure is never constant; it varies at elevation and from location to location. Things would be much simpler if there was a standard air pressure all over the country. There isn't, but to help matters along the UK is divided up into Altimeter Setting Regions. When flying through various areas the datum for calculating aircraft height is Mean Sea Level (MSL), and the UK Altimeter Setting Regions use this as their datum. The general idea being that as the aircraft leaves one region and enters another, the altimeter is adjusted to the new setting, and 'sticky-up' parts of the ground may be avoided with confidence.

QNH

This regional altimeter setting is known in ATC terms as the QNH –

Q-codes being a method of wireless telegraphy (Morse code) shorthand. Each Q-code representing both a statement or a question, depending whether it was suffixed with a question mark or not. If you've listened to airband radio at an airport you will have heard Tower passing the QNH to arriving/departing aircraft, e.g. '. . . . And the QNH is one-zero-one-eight'

Sometimes the actual altimeter setting region name is used, such as: '. . . . one-zero-one-eight on the Barnsley.'

So, just to recap, QNH is the *local* barometric pressure based on height above mean sea level. QNH *does not* mean height above the ground at that location. For that datum there is another meaningless Q-code; QFE.

QFE

If the pilot has set the local QNH on the adjustment sub-scale of her altimeter when coming into land, the altimeter will not necessarily read the true height of the aircraft above the runway. Even when she's landed her altimeter could still be pretending that the aircraft is 300 feet high! Unless, of course, the elevation of the airport just happened to

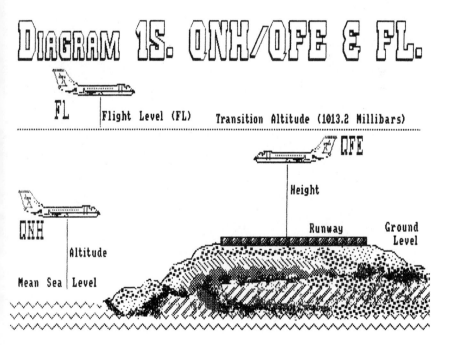

DIAGRAM 15. QNH/QFE & FL.

FL — Flight Level (FL)   Transition Altitude (1013.2 Millibars)

QFE

Height

QNH

Altitude

Runway   Ground Level

Mean Sea | Level

be exactly the same as mean sea level. Diagram 15 summarises this information for you.

To give a pilot a better indication of height above the actual runway, ATC will directly measure air pressure at the airport, so the datum then becomes the elevation of the airport, and not mean sea level. This type of barometric pressure is known as the QFE. On final approach Tower will pass the QFE to the pilot. The altimeter will be adjusted to this setting, and this time she'll get an accurate readout of aircraft height above the actual runway itself. When the aircraft has landed, the altimeter will now read zero. By the way, aircraft carrying radio altimeters have no use for the QFE reading as they rely on their instrument to measure height above the runway.

I've been sprinkling the words Height and Altitude around fairly loosely. In actual fact, in aviation they both have clear definitions. When the QFE has been set on the altimeter, then that aircraft's vertical distance above the ground is always referred to as HEIGHT. If the QNH has been set, then instead of height, ALTITUDE is used in its place. This is important to we airband listeners because depending on whether we hear the words QNH or QFE we can tell if an aircraft is approaching to land, or merely over-flying.

Flight Level

So far we have QNH, barometric pressure above mean sea level, and QFE, barometric pressure above local elevation. There is a third type of barometric pressure, only this time the reference datum is entirely fictitious: Flight Level. When an aircraft is flying within an airway, accurate height knowledge is important. Aircraft have to maintain a vertical separation of 1,000 feet below 24,500 feet. If the QNH (which becomes more and more inaccurate as height increases) was to be used for aircraft within airways, complying with an ATC instruction to climb to 19,000 feet would be a hit and miss affair – relying on QNH would mean that you could be anywhere between 18,000 to 20,000 feet, and that is simply intolerable.

To circumvent the shortcomings of QNH, aircraft set a standard 1013.2 millibars on the altimeter, which represents the 'average' air pressure at mean sea level, around the world. This standard setting is actually no more accurate than the QNH, but that really doesn't matter at all because *all* aircraft will adjust their altimeters to this standard setting when *above* the Transition Altitude. An aircraft flying at 19,000 feet may not be at exactly 19,000; but what the pilot does know is that the aircraft above him will be exactly 1,000 feet away, because they are both using the same altimeter reference. And that's important for maintaining the separation standards.

Transition Altitude

The Transition Altitude is the boundary on the way up, where alti-meters are changed from the QNH to the Standard 1013.2 millibars. Unfortunately, there may well be a standard altimeter setting, but there's no standard for where the Transition Altitude begins! It can begin as low as 3,000 feet in some countries, while in others it may be 19,000 feet. It can vary within the same country, and even from airport to airport! Coming down, the point where the change from the Standard Setting is changed to QNH is the Transition Level. Where 'height' was used while QFE was set, and 'altitude' for QNH; when the Standard has been set, 'Flight Levels' are used. Prior to the Transition Altitude, height and altitude are measured in thousands of feet. With flight levels, the thousands are truncated by lopping off the last two zeros. For example:

25,000 feet in altitude becomes Flight Level (FL) 250. 19,000 feet becomes FL 190. 37,000 feet is FL 370.

The Airband Listener

I have gone into the subject of the aircraft's altimeter in detail because what setting the aircraft is using can tell you a lot about that flight. If you're hearing 'QFE' then it's a good bet that the aircraft's going to land. QNH tells us that the aircraft is outside of controlled airspace, flying VFR; but it could also be climbing up into an airway, or des-cending out of one. Once we hear the words 'Flight Level', then we know that the aircraft is flying above the Transition Altitude, most probably within an airway and by association, must be flying IFR.

Flying The Airways

We are now familiar with an aircraft departing under the airport's ATC until clear of the area, and then being handed-over to En-route ATC. When flying in airways, aircraft navigate from VOR beacon to beacon, so quite a lot of ATC instructions revolve around beacon names.

'Midland 900 descend flight level 110 55 DME Pole Hill.'
'Roger, Midland 900 is leaving 190 for one-one-zero, five-five Pole Hill.'

Trans: Flight Midland 900 please descend to flight level 110 at 55 miles distance from the Pole Hill VHF Omni-Range beacon. The pilot responds by saying that he's leaving flight level 190 (19,000 feet) for FL 110 (11,000 feet), and will be at that height when he's 55 miles from

137

the Pole Hill VOR beacon, which is situated to the north-east of Manchester Airport.

Co-sited with the VOR beacon is another device very similar to radar, called Distance Measuring Equipment (DME). By firing radio signals at each other and timing the returns, the aircraft can work out how far away the VOR/DME is, and whether the aircraft is flying towards or away from it. As in the example above, En-route ATC often make use of DME when passing instructions, ordering a change of heading or altitude at so many miles DME (beacon name).

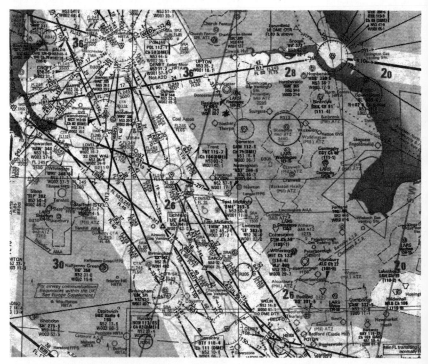

Aerad Low Altitude chart (EFF) (*reproduced by kind permission of the British Airways Aerad*)

Position Reports

Along airway routes are standard reporting points, some compulsory – usually at airway junctions – and some 'on request' where the aircraft may be asked to report. With the growing adoption of Secondary Surveillance Radar (SSR), which provides ATC with a computer-generated display of the aircraft's heading, altitude and identification, an aircraft may be told to 'Omit position reports', as position information is perfectly clear on the SSR display. Where position reports are required, they take the form of:

1 Callsign of aircraft
2 Current position
3 Time now (in minutes passed)
4 Flight Level
5 Next position headed for
6 ETA at that position

'Foxbat Zero-one'	'Midland 900'
'Sapco'	'Finch'
'45'	'10'
'FL40'	'FL245'
'Buzad'	'Hemel'
'05'	'20'

Trans: Aircraft, who's callsign is Foxbat Zero-one is abeam the SAPCO reporting point at 45 minutes (past the current hour) at Flight Level 45 (4,500 feet). The next position will be another reporting point called BUZAD, and the aircraft expects to arrive there at 5 minutes (past the next hour).

As aircraft fly within the airways system they are passed from controller to controller. On descent from an airway to airport approach, En-route ATC establishes the aircraft near either a VOR or NDB beacon, and passes control over to Airport Approach. After take-off, and once clear of traffic around the airport's Special Rules Area, Airport Approach or Departure Control (depending on the size and staffing of the terminal) will instruct the pilot to 'Contact London', passing control of the flight over to En-route ATC.

AIR TRAFFIC CONTROL NAVIGATION AIDS

Non-Directional (NDB) Beacons

This radio device is the simplest of all radionavigation equipment. It is used as a centre marker for airways with a range about 100 miles, and as a combined Locator-Outer Marker (LOM) beacon for airport approach and landings, with a limited range of around 12 miles. Non-Directional Beacons transmit their signal in the Long/Medium Wave frequency bands, between 200 and 700kHz. At precise intervals the beacon identifies itself by transmitting a three letter callsign in Morse code. As its name suggests, the beacon transmits its signal equally around all compass points, and can be intercepted from any direction.

The aircraft's ADF (Automatic Direction Finding) aerials sense the direction of the NDB in much the same way as when you turn a domestic transistor radio, tuned to the long or medium waveband, from

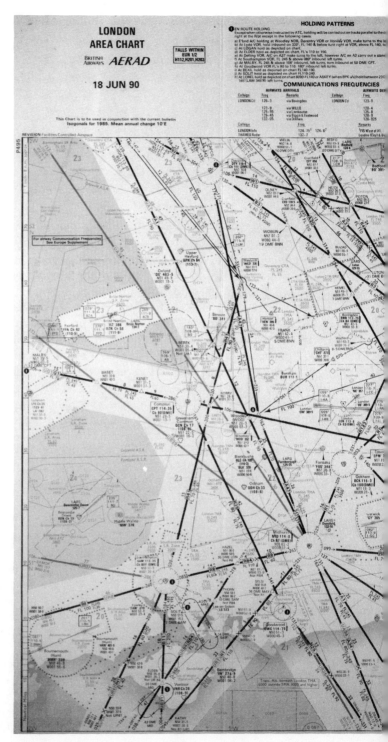

Low Altitude CAA Airways chart
(*reproduced by kind permission of the CAA*)

AIRSPACE RESTRICTIONS

side to side. The effect is the received station will grow weaker, being weakest when the radio's internal ferrite aerial is pointing directly at the distant transmitter, and strongest when the set's aerial is broadside-on to it. Where the signal is weakest is known as the null position, and the aircraft's ADF aerials, on establishing the null point, pass this information to the flight deck, where it is presented to the pilot on a Radio Magnetic Indicator (RMI). The RMI is a compass with an extra pointer which indicates the null position of the NDB as established by the ADF antennas, and shows the pilot the position of the aircraft in relationship to the beacon.

NDBs are prone to interference from other beacons in the very crowded LW band, and also from atmospheric sources, such as cumulonimbus (CB) cloud formations with their associated high electrical activity. A pilot may well find his RMI pointing to the nearest thundercloud, rather than the NDB! For this reason NDBs as airways markers are being replaced by VORs.

VHF Omni-Range (VOR) Beacons

Like the NDB, VORs transmit their signal omnidirectionally, the difference being that it is possible with a VOR to tell from which particular direction the signal is coming from. VORs are used as airway centreline markers and as reporting points along them; their range being some 200 nautical miles. They transmit in the VHF navigation sub-band, between 108.000–117.900mHz. Without going into too much technical detail, the VOR transmits two types of signal, one AM and

Mayfield VOR/DME array (*reproduced by kind permission of the CAA*)

the other FM. The transmitted VOR radio signal is made to rotate electronically, producing the same effect as if the aerial was being spun rapidly at 30 revolutions per second. At Magnetic North the two signals appear as one, but as the signals work their way around the compass points, the AM part of the signal begins to first lag behind the FM, and then lead it, until Magnetic North, where they're back together again (in phase).

A VOR receiver in the aircraft can detect these phase differences, and work out its bearing in relation to the beacon, so instead of just pointing in the general direction, as with an NDB, VOR tells the pilot the precise magnetic bearing the aircraft would have to fly assuming that it was heading for the VOR. The bearings from the VOR are known as Radials, because they radiate outwards from the beacon like the spokes of a wheel. Radials are referred to directly by ATC, such as:

'. . . . pick-up the 090 (magnetic East) radial, Pole Hill . . . .'. (See Diagram 13, p131.)

Information from the aircraft's VOR receivers is presented to the pilot either on the RMI, in the same way as NDB, or on the Horizontal Situation Indicator (HSI) as a Beam Bar. To maintain the aircraft on the VOR course the captain simply keeps the beam bar centred on the aircraft's heading index on the main compass. Deviation from the VOR radial left or right of track will push the beam bar to the left or the right of the heading index (see Diagram 16). VORs are more reliable than

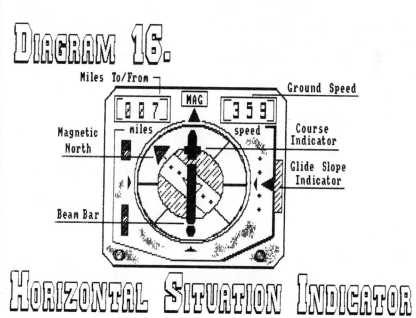

DIAGRAM 16.

HORIZONTAL SITUATION INDICATOR

NDBs because atmospheric noise affects Amplitude more than Frequency. This is why radio signals on domestic receivers sound much 'quieter' on VHF FM, than they do on LW and MW, which both use AM.

Distance Measuring Equipment (DME)

Associated with, and co-sited alongside VOR beacons is Distance Measuring Equipment (DME). As its name implies, the DME tells an aircraft its distance to, or from a particular VOR. The equipment is a type of radar, transmitting in the UHF band – 962–1213mHz. A DME transponder in the aircraft will send out a stream of radio pulses on radio frequency x, which the ground-based DME receives. In reply, DME transmits its own series of RF pulses on radio frequency y. The aircraft will *only* respond to radio signals received on frequency 'y'; and the ground-based DME will *only* reply to signals on frequency 'x'. Both 'x' and 'y' are separated by 63mHz to avoid the aircraft receiving its own radio signal, reflected back off the ground, which would throw a spanner into the works.

Because the speed of an electro-magnetic (radio) wave is known very precisely, the time differences between the aircraft and DME radio signals are calculated, and the result is the common distance between them. The DME receivers on the aircraft work out whether the aircraft is approaching or leaving the ground-based DME, presenting the distance (in nautical miles) as either *from* or *to*.

Like the ILS Localiser and Glide Slope combination, VOR and DME are 'paired' together. Selecting a VOR frequency on the aircraft's VOR receivers automatically selects the appropriate UHF DME channel as well.

Primary Radar

Aviation makes use of many forms of radar (*RA*dio *D*irection *A*nd *R*ange). Primary Radar is perhaps the simplest form, and the one most people readily identify. Simply, 'pulsed' radio waves are transmitted, and in between the transmit pulse the radar receiver listens for any reflections. Returned radar pulses are displayed on a cathode ray tube – CRT, usually in Plan Position Indicator form – which is a phosphorous 'arm' sweeping around the circular display of the CRT. Reflections appear as a 'blip' on the screen as the bright trace sweeps over them. The centre of the PPI display represents the radar aerial, and where the blips appear on the screen is the bearing of the radar target from the aerial. How far away from the centre of the PPI display the blips appears is the target's distance from the radar aerial (see Diagram 17).

DIAGRAM 17. RADAR DISPLAYS.

Circular 'Sweep' Trace

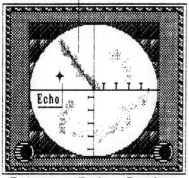

Primary Radar Display

Aircraft, FL, Number & Airport

SSR Visual Display Unit

So primary radar gives us basic information about direction and distance of a target, but isn't much help with an aircraft's altitude, and identification. Approach Control at the airport make use of primary radar, to warn them of aircraft flying in the airport's controlled airspace, and aircraft coming in to land. Before Approach can make any decisions based on his radar display, he has to positively identify all the blips.

Other uses for primary radar are: weather radar, carried in the nose of an aircraft – the RF pulses are reflected off water droplets in cloud formations, and warn the pilot of any cumulo-nimbus cloud along the track; Precision Approach Radar (PAR), an alternative to ILS (see later), PAR is used as a final approach aid, guiding an aircraft down onto the runway with considerable accuracy. The system is thought too expensive for civil airports, but military airfields have it.

Secondary Surveillance Radar

Secondary Surveillance Radar (SSR) offers all the features of primary radar plus many others. It works in a similar way to DME. A ground-based radar transponder emits RF pulses on frequency A. The aircraft's SSR transponder receives the pulses and transmits its answering burst on frequency B. The frequencies 'A' and 'B' being widely spaced so that any reflection from the aircraft of frequency A's original signal cannot be confused with the aircraft's response on frequency B.

With primary radar only a percentage of the original RF pulse is

145

reflected back off the aircraft, which can often give a weak, fuzzy echo on the CRT display from certain types of aircraft. With SSR, the returned blip is much stronger, providing a diamond clear synthetic echo on the Radar Visual Display Unit (RVDU). SSR signals aren't presented in the same way as primary radar; they are computer-processed first. The SSR transponder in the aircraft has various modes of operation which are triggered according to what the ground SSR station wants to know.

The usual SSR display on the RVDU is a small cross which represents the returned radar blip of the aircraft, and a short series of trailing dots indicating the track of the aircraft. Every few seconds the image is updated, and the cross and dot trail move across the screen. Added to the synthetic radar echo and dot-tail on the display screen are: the

Heathrow Airport, Secondary Surveillance Radar array (*reproduced by kind permission of the CAA*)

aircraft's flight number and destination airport, both of which are stored within ATC computers when the original flight plan was first registered. At a glance a Radar or Approach director can tell from the RVDU which aircraft is which, the heading (course steered) and distance from the airport.

Aircraft flying outside of controlled airspace and who also carry SSR equipment set a standard squawk code of 4321. Where there is more than one aircraft using this code the controller has to sort out which blip belongs to which aircraft. She does this by asking a particular pilot to: 'Squawk Ident, please'.

The pilot hits a switch on his SSR transponder, and one of the blips on the Radar Controller's RVDU begins to flash and brighten, positively identifying the aircraft's synthetic echo. This is SSR Mode A. Mode B on the aircraft's SSR links the transponder to the altimeter, giving ground ATC details about the aircraft's altitude – something which has to be passed by R/T when using primary radar.

The advantages of SSR are: it provides ATC with a very clear and sharp synthetic echo, and information about destination, altitude, identification and routing. You can often hear airport ATC request that an aircraft squawk a certain code, such as, 'Squawk 4765 please'. The pilot will set the code on his SSR transponder, enabling his aircraft to be recognised uniquely by airport radar or approach/departure controllers. Various 'squawk' codes are assigned for certain purposes. For example, Squawk 7700 denotes an on-board emergency; while Squawk 7500 warns ATC units worldwide of a hijack attempt!

Secondary Surveillance Radar still has much development potential. Experiments are on-going into a system by which an aircraft's SSR will continuously transmit information about heading, altitude, and speed while in flight, warning other aircraft of its presence.

Instrument Landing System (ILS)

There are three main parts to the ILS. A horizontal radio beam which marks the exact centreline of the runway, extending outwards from the airport to around 20 miles, and called the 'Localiser'. A vertical radio beam indicating the correct descent profile of 3 degrees (I'll explain this in a minute), which extends around 10 miles out from the runway, called the 'Glide Slope'. And finally radio marker beacons, firing their signals upwards in a fan-shaped pattern. The Outer Marker Beacon is situated around 4–10 miles from the runway threshold, at 1 mile the Middle Marker, and on the runway threshold the Inner Marker Beacon – although this has virtually disappeared now, current landing speeds making it all but impossible to register its presence!

Descent Profile

When coming in to land an aircraft has to lose height so that by the time it has arrived at the runway threshold (the beginning of the runway) it should be around 10–20 feet above it, and can then flair-out and touch down firmly enough to make sure the wheels bite the tarmac, but not with a massive jolt to upset the passengers and possibly damage the aircraft. The aeroplane will adopt a descent profile of 3 degrees so that it loses height at the rate of 300 feet per mile. At the Outer Marker, an aircraft will be at around 1200 feet – 300 × 4 = 1200 for a 4 mile Outer Marker; or at 3,000 feet for a 10 mile Outer Marker Beacon.

The Localiser

The localiser looks like a surrealist's idea of a garden fence, usually painted bright yellow so that an aircraft can tell what it's just hit if it over-runs on the runway. It's a large antenna array sited at the 'windward' end of the runway, (the end opposite that used for take-offs and landings) and at right angles to it. The localiser squirts two beams of RF on the same frequency (between 108–112mHz) down the exact centre of the runway, modulating one beam with a tone of 'A' Hz and the other with a tone of 'B' Hz. On the aircraft a special ILS receiver

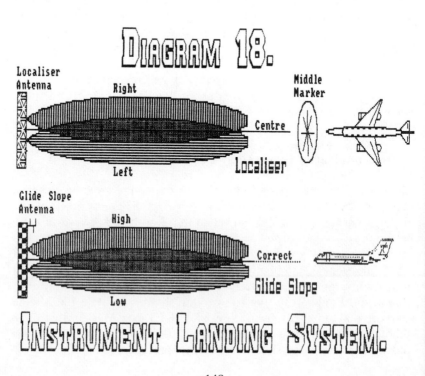

picks up the signal from the localiser, and from the received signal strength can indicate on the Horizontal Situation Indicator instrument on the flight-deck whether the aircraft is to the left, the right, or exactly lined up with the runway centreline.

Glide Slope

The glide slope transmitter works in almost exactly the same way as the localiser, except that the beams are vertical, not horizontal, and the frequency is in the Ultra High Frequency (UHF) range. The glide slope aerial is positioned at the 'downwind' end of the runway, close to the threshold and offset to one side. Like VOR/DME beacons the localiser and glide slope frequencies are paired, so that selecting one will automatically select the other on the aircraft's ILS receiving equipment. The ILS will identify itself using a three/four letter name (usually the abbreviated airport name) in Morse code (see Diagram 18).

Marker Beacons

The marker beacons are positioned on the extended centreline of the runway, in line with the ILS, and they tell the pilot how far to touch down. Approach, in the control tower, will ask the pilot to report when he has passed over the Outer Marker, so that he can ensure the approach path is clear, and can pass the pilot to Tower.

All marker beacons transmit on the same VHF frequency, 75mHz. They fire a fan-shaped beam of RF vertically. The Outer Marker is modulated with Morse dashes of low frequency. When the aircraft flies over it, the pilot and co-pilot hear these low frequency dashes in their headsets, and a blue lamp on the instrument panel of the flight deck flashes in synchrony with them.

At the Middle Marker, medium frequency alternating Morse dots and dashes are heard on the flight deck, and this time an amber lamp flashes. At the Inner Marker (where used), the Morse modulation changes to high pitched dots coupled with a scintillating white lamp.

Locator Outer Marker (LOM)

Often the airport's Outer Marker beacon is replaced with a combined Airport Locator NDB and ILS Outer Marker to make up a Locator Outer Marker (LOM). ATC often refer to this type of beacon when positioning an aircraft for an ILS approach. The aircraft may join the airport circuit 'Downwind' and be told to: 'Report beacon out-bound'.

The aircraft is flying parallel to the runway, but in the opposite direction to the active end. As it passes the LOM outbound, the pilot calls Approach Control and tells him that the beacon's passed out-bound. Approach will then 'clear' the aircraft for a Procedure Turn, and ask the pilot to report the LOM in-bound. Which simply means that the aircraft turns around and flies towards the runway, re-passing the LOM beacon for a second time, but this time on the way in to intercept the ILS.

How It All Works

An approaching aircraft will have been descended out of an airway by En-route ATC, positioned near an airport VOR, LOM or NDB, and then passed over to the airport's Approach Controller. Approach's aim

Instrument Landing System, Bournemouth (Hurn) Airport (*reproduced by kind permission of the CAA*)

is to direct the incoming aircraft to within 30 degrees of the ILS at around twelve miles from the runway threshold, by passing the pilot radar vectors to steer.

At around twelve miles, the pilot has only to make a gentle 30 degrees turn to intercept the localiser signal or, as the pilots say 'To Establish'. Output from the ILS receiver on-board is displayed on the Horizontal Situation Indicator (HSI) instrument on the flight-deck, which shows a beam bar running vertically up the centre of its display, which represents the localiser signal. If the beam bar is pushed away from the centre of the HSI over to the right, then the aircraft is too far *left* of the centreline. Too far right of the runway centreline shows on the HSI as the beam bar being pushed over to the *left*.

Bearing in mind that the pilot quite possibly cannot see anything of the ground, much less the runway, he can either fly the aircraft by hand with respect to the Horizontal Situation Indicator (keeping the beam bar centred) – or let the aircraft fly itself down the localiser beam by linking the HSI to the autopilot. Once safely established on the localiser the pilot aims to fly slightly below the level of the glide slope beam, so that he can intercept it from below, at around ten miles from touchdown.

At ten miles to touchdown the Glide Slope Indicator on the Horizontal Situation Indicator becomes 'live' and the aircraft becomes fully established on the ILS. On hearing the low-pitched Morse dah's and seeing the flashing blue light on the flight-deck, the pilot duly reports passing the Outer Marker to Approach in the control tower. Normally, Approach would now tell the pilot to QSY (change the frequency) from the Approach radio frequency to that of the Tower, passing control to the ATCO responsible for landings and take-offs.

Providing the airport is suitably equipped (ILS class 3) and the aircraft has the capability (and company permission!) the aircraft can actually fly down the ILS on autopilot and land itself! But, landing an aircraft in poor – or even no – visibility is still only half the story. The aircraft still has to clear the runway, and taxi back to the ramp or stand to unload passengers etc. so a highly sophisticated lighting system is needed to guide the aircraft.

OCEANIC AIR TRAFFIC CONTROL

Trans-Oceanic Air Traffic

The statistics make very interesting reading. In 1989 more than 25 million passengers were flown across the North Atlantic Ocean in 160,000 commercial flights. During the peak summer months more than 60 flights an hour were crossing Shanwick Oceanic's boundaries; and

750 flights per day were taking place. Civil and military transatlantic flights for the year totalled 189,000!

With this huge number of flights involved, added to the fact that control of such aircraft over the North Atlantic Ocean can only ever be at 'second-hand', because there are no airways and no radar, the potential for a major catastrophe is only too real! Luckily, it hasn't happened yet.

There aren't any obliging VORs in the middle of the Atlantic Ocean to inform the aircraft's avionics where it is. Neither are there any friendly En-route ATC controllers sitting on marker buoys in the middle of the sea with a handheld transceiver, waiting for the pilot's call. In fact, there isn't much of anything, apart from the odd ship! Two hundred miles out from the coastline and an aircraft's three VHF 'boxes' aren't going to be of much use. The requirements of controlled airspace are not cancelled once the aircraft leaves the mainland for the Atlantic, although they are slightly different.

Shanwick Oceanic Air Traffic Control Centre

There isn't actually a place called Shanwick; it's a telescoping of two real place names: SHANnon in Ireland, and PrestWICK, in Scotland.

Shanwick Oceanic Control Room, Atlantic House (*reproduced by kind permission of the SCATCC*)

'Shanwick (pronounced Shan-WIK) Oceanic' as it is known as, is an Oceanic Air Traffic Control Centre (OATCC), responsible for the control of aircraft en-route to North America over the North Atlantic Ocean. It has two parts, the main control centre, which is based in Atlantic House, near Prestwick airport in Ayrshire, Scotland, and Shanwick Aeradio – a radio station at Ballygirreen near Shannon, Ireland.

The boundaries of Shanwick OCA are:

Southern: 45 degrees North Latitude (bordering with Santa Maria and New York OCAs).
Northern: 61 degrees North Latitude (border with Reykjavic OCA).
Western: 30 degrees West Longitude (border with Gander OCA).
The Eastern boundary is within the London/Scottish FIR/UIRs.
(See chart below.)

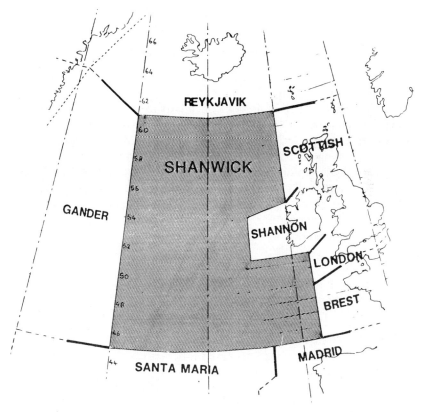

Atlantic Oceanic Control Areas (*reproduced by kind permission of the SCATCC*)

Trans-Oceanic Flights

Flights leaving from the UK to North America take-off around noon, arriving Stateside around 1400 local time. Flights from the US to Britain and Europe leave in the early evening, arriving in the UK around 0700 local.

Although there is no radar, no VHF and no airways, Shanwick's airspace is still controlled because it is a Minimum Navigation Performance Specification (MNPS) area. Just like controlled airspace over the mainland, prior permission must be asked for and granted before an aircraft may enter Shanwick's OCA, and this is done in the same way as controlled airspace – by the filing of a flight plan. Details of the flight, time, altitude, type of aircraft etc. are lodged at Atlantic House, where all the details are entered into the Flight Data Processing System computer, which is the real 'brains' behind Oceanic Control, and we'll be meeting it again later. Having 'asked' for permission to enter Shanwick by entering a flight plan, the aircraft must then meet MNPS standards.

Minimum Navigation Performance Specification

MNPS airspace over the North Atlantic starts at 27,500 feet and goes up to 40,000 feet – Flight Levels 275–400. Within this airspace aircraft must have navigation equipment on board to a standard specified by the International Civil Aviation Authority (ICAO), which usually means at least *two* INS or OMEGA systems (prime & backup).

Inertial Navigation System (INS) offers a high degree of navigational accuracy and reliability. As control of aircraft in the Oceanic Control Area is based purely on procedure, accurate navigation is essential. Should an aircraft stray from a track due to faulty equipment, or erroneous navigation, then the dangers inherent in such busy airspace explain themselves.

The Organised Track System

Although there aren't any airways over the North Atlantic, there are special routes known as Tracks. Allocating and organising the track system is based upon the needs of jet aircraft and the weather conditions over the ocean on that day. Because of the nature of the jet engine, jet-powered aircraft need to fly high, between 29,000 to 37,000 feet, to obtain the best ratio between speed and fuel economy. At lower altitudes more fuel is burned by the engines.

At these heights a phenomenom called *Jetstream* is encountered, which is a layer of fast moving air around 2–3 miles deep, 2–4 hundred miles wide and over a 1,000 miles long. Winds in excess of 200 knots have been recorded within the centre. Aircraft must avoid heading into the jetstream or they will find their fuel figures catastrophic. On the other hand, manoeuvering your aircraft so that the jetstream is blowing under your tail can save you a lot of fuel and cut down on flying time!

Weather reports are put together twice a day from meteorological ships on the ocean, weather satellites and coastal stations by Shanwick Oceanic, on this side of the Atlantic, and by Gander Oceanic (Newfoundland) on the other. Information such as the position of the jetstream, wind-speed and direction are compiled, and from this data the tracks for that day are nominated. With most of the American flights en-route overnight, Gander OCA takes responsibility for the night-time tracks and Shanwick for the day.

The track information is distributed directly by Shanwick to Oceanic Air Traffic Control Centres and airports in this country who handle transatlantic flights, such as the London airports, Manchester International and Prestwick. Track information is also broadcast daily, between 0900 and 1900 hours GMT on a frequency of 133.800mHz.

Naming The Tracks

Around six tracks a day are nominated. For westbound routes they are labelled from A–C; using the ICAO phonetic alphabet: Tracks Alpha, Bravo, Charlie, Delta, Echo, and Foxtrot. Track Alpha is always the most northerly one – whatever its latitude. The next-most northerly is nominated Track Bravo, then next Track Charlie, and so on to Track Foxtrot which is the most southerly track on that day.

On eastbound routes the tracks are nominated as U–Z, or Uniform, Victor, Whisky, X-Ray, Yankee and Track Zulu. Track Uniform is the westbound's most northerly – whatever its latitude, the next-most northerly is Track Victor, while the southernmost track is always Track Zulu. Part of a typical track information broadcast by Shanwick on 133.800mHz sounds something like this.

'This is Shanwick Aeradio. The North Atlantic Organised Tracks for the sixteenth of June nineteen-eighty-nine. From twelve to nineteen hundred Golf Mike time. Track Alpha – five-two North, one-five West, five-two North, two-zero West, five-two North, three-zero West, five-two North, four-zero West, five-two North, five-zero West, St Anthony.'

'Track Bravo – four-nine North, zero-eight West, five-zero North, two-zero West, five-zero North, three-zero West, four-nine North, four-zero West, four-seven North, five-zero West, Color. This is Shanwick Aeradio, good day.'

Position Reporting Points

Having received confirmation and clearance of the required track from Shanwick (in this case, Track Bravo), the captain of an aircraft enters the five latitudes and longitudes into the INS, carefully checked by the crew. Each latitude and longitude mentioned is a waypoint, a direction in which the aircraft must fly; all of these waypoints making up a transatlantic crossing course, called 'Track Bravo'.

The aircraft will first penetrate Oceanic airspace at 49 degrees North latitude, 8 degrees West longitude, the first waypoint. At every succeeding waypoint the captain has to pass a Position Report by HF (upper) Single Sideband Radio Telephony, to Shanwick, at the Ballygirreen Radio Station. Position reports consist of the following elements.

Callsign	identification of the flight/aircraft
Present position	latitude/longitude or name
Time over	GMT arrived at 'present position'
Flight level	altitude of aircraft
Next position	latitude/longitude or name of next waypoint
ETA	estimated time over next waypoint
NEXT	'lat/long' or name of next-but-one waypoint
Additional	any further information – weather etc

For example:	'Foxbat zero-one. five-zero North, two-zero West zero-one-zero-zero flight level three-seven-zero estimate five-zero North, three-zero West zero-two-zero-zero. Next. Five-zero North, four-zero West. Over.' (No additional information.)

Oceanic Clearances

Just as aircraft in controlled airspace over the mainland need clearance to enter, an aircraft wanting to cross the North Atlantic has to obtain clearance from Shanwick before entering the OCA. A flight plan will have been lodged with Atlantic House, and they will have activated the plan an hour before the flight was due to take-off, and distributed the Flight Progress Strip (FPS) to the relevant ATC centres and airports. The FDPS at Atlantic House will have already warned controllers there of any conflict between different companies' wants on the day, or any conflict of the required spatial separation between aircraft (see Separation Standards, later). Passengers board, the captain spools-up the engines, and the aircraft leaves the departure airport on its SID route heading for Ireland. When in VHF range of Shanwick, the LATCC controller will advise the captain to: 'Continue with Shanwick on one-two-seven decimal six-five.' Unlike normal VHF R/T procedures, where services have their own unique frequency, and others have frequencies allocated on a regional basis, *all* aircraft calling for Oceanic Clearance will do so on the same frequency. For aircraft registered east of 30 degrees West longitude – Britain and Europe – this frequency is 127.650mHz. For aircraft registered west of 30 degrees West longitude, the USA and Canada etc. 123.950mHz is used. An aircraft calling for clearance must call before passing west of 2 degrees West longitude to allow Shanwick time to sort out the clearance. For aircraft taking-off from an airport already west of 2 degrees West, they must call as early as possible.

Flight 'Foxbat Zero-One' calls 'Clearance' at Atlantic House, on 127.650mHz. The Delivery Controller recalls Foxbat Zero-one's flight plan from the FDPS, checks again for 'conflicts', confirms the Mach number (see later) and requested flight level. If everything is OK, then 'Clearance' for the proposed routing is passed back to Foxbat Zero-One. For example:

'Foxbat Zero-One is cleared to JFK – New York by Track Bravo. Flight level three-seven-zero – Mach eight-seven cruise. Track Bravo is:
Four-nine North – zero-eight West. Five-zero North – two-zero West. Five-zero North – three-zero West. Four-nine North – four-zero West. Four-seven North – five-zero West. Color. Good day.'

The captain of Foxbat Zero-One reads back the clearance, and aims the aircraft for the Ocean entry point at 49 degrees North latitude, 08 degrees West longitude. The FDPS computer at Shanwick passes details of the aircraft's course etc. to all ATCCs who will handle the flight, and begins its own monitoring service.

But suppose that the clearance is *not* OK? There might be a conflict within the FDPS computer, either of requested track, or an impingement on separation standards. What then? The software engineering of the FDPS computer allows for an amount of leeway. Controllers will interrogate the FDPS for alternatives and pass these onto the captain of the aircraft requesting the clearance. Discussion will take place and a mutually acceptable solution will be worked out to everyone's satisfaction: usually! The aircraft might have to 'stooge around' for a while though, while the matter is resolved; but it usually is.

Unlike LATCC, or airport control, where the Air Traffic Control Officers make direct contact with pilots on VHF R/T, Shanwick can only receive and pass messages at second-hand, using the radio station at Ballygirreen, Ireland; Shanwick Aeradio.

Shanwick Aeradio – Ballygirreen

Shanwick Aeradio – which is both name and radio R/T callsign – is the communications link for the Shanwick Ocean Control Area. It passes messages to aircraft over the North Atlantic Ocean using High Frequency (HF) R/T, using the Single Sideband (SSB) mode, specifically, Upper Sideband. An aircraft will use two frequencies from its family group, a primary and a secondary. Should an aircraft experience any problems with the primary frequency, a switch is made to the back-up secondary.

On receipt of a message from an aircraft over the ocean, Shanwick Aeradio passes it on to Atlantic House via telex. Any messages to the aircraft will come to the radio station via telex and be relayed to the aircraft on HF SSB R/T. Which begs the question: why can't Atlantic House use the radio equipment themselves, and 'cut out the middleman'?

I have explained elsewhere in the Handbook the problems people can experience listening to HF SSB transmissions, so briefly, Air Traffic Control Officers (ATCOs) are professional controllers of aircraft and *not* professional radio operators. The radio station at Ballygirreen, however, *is* staffed by professional radio operators, who have the experience and ability to deal with all the problems HF SSB radio telephony can produce.

Messages from aircraft to Shanwick Aeradio fall into one of the following categories.

POS	Position Report (waypoints, 10 degrees or 1 hour)
RCL	Request For Clearance (climb, descend, change heading)
RBK	Read Back ('readbacks' to confirm ATC instructions)
RPE	Report Of Revised Time Estimate
TAM	Technical Acknowledgement Message (engineering etc.)
SELCAL	SELective CALling (tone-encoded squelch test)
EMG	Emergency Messages (Mayday)
MIS	Miscellaneous (anything else)

Mach Numbers

The standard instrument on an aircraft for measuring its speed through the air is the Air Speed Indicator (ASI). The ASI works accurately within a narrow range – outside that range it becomes dangerously inaccurate. As control over aircraft on the North Atlantic Track system is by procedure, one of which is that aircraft must maintain 15 minutes' flying time between flights, aircraft *must* know their precise speed. Aircraft at cruise level over the Atlantic will be anywhere from 32–37,000 feet: the ASI is unreliable above 28,000. Therefore there has to be a new system for measuring an aircraft's speed at the cruise level.

Instead of the air speed indicator, the speed of an aircraft at cruise level is given as a ratio between the True Airspeed (TAS) and the 'local' speed of sound. It is expressed as a Mach Number, and for subsonic aircraft is usually given as a percentage of the speed of sound, eg. Mach .81–Mach .87. A Mach number of .75 would be seventy-five per cent of the (local) speed of sound. Maximum Mach for a Boeing 747 Jetliner is around Mach .90: Concorde flies at Mach 2 (no decimal point!), but there are special arrangements for Concorde's supersonic flights as we shall see.

Separation Standards

With the absence of radar monitoring over the North Atlantic, control is by Procedure – standard ways of doing things. Aircraft safety in controlled airspace (of which MNPS is a type) is maintained by keeping the aircraft apart: generating a safety zone above, below, in front of and behind an aircraft. The distances by which aircraft are kept apart is the Separation Standard, and is varied according to: radio telephony, radar and navigation equipment carried by the aircraft, the type of airspace flown in.

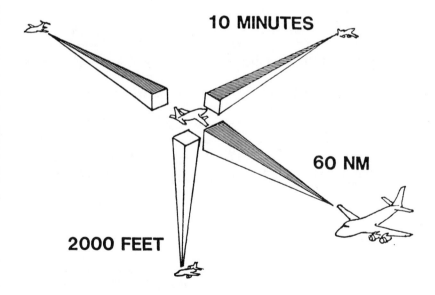

MNPS Separation Standards (*reproduced by kind permission of the SCATCC*)

Separation: Minimum Navigation Performance Specification Airspace

Within MNPS airspace (27,500–40,000 feet) aircraft are required to be:

Clear of other 'traffic' for 2,000 feet vertically
Have a lateral (horizontal) clearance of 60 nautical miles
Minimum of 10 flying minutes behind another aircraft.*

* This doesn't necessarily mean that an aircraft 'behind' will be ten minutes away at any one time. Some aircraft are faster than others, so taking the relative speeds into consideration has to be done to maintain the 10-minute rule.

Below MNPS airspace – 27,500 feet, an aircraft must be:

Clear of other 'traffic' for 1,000 feet vertically
Have a lateral separation of 120 nautical miles
Minimum of 30 minutes flying time behind another aircraft.

Special arrangements and routes are used for aircraft flying VFR outside of MNPS airspace. They are often subject to the regulations of the various Ocean Control Areas through which they will pass.

Crossing The Pond

Foxbat Zero-One has its oceanic clearance, has left the domestic airways system and has climbed to cruise level and throttled back the engines. The first waypoint has been transmitted to Shanwick Aeradio and a meal is being served on the flight-deck. Around every hour the First Officer will transmit the aircraft's position, and listen for the SelCal in between.

When the aircraft arrives at waypoint 50 degrees North, 30 degrees West, which marks the 'middle' of the Atlantic crossing, and also marks Shanwick Oceanic's Western border with Gander Oceanic, the First Officer passes the position report to both Gander and Shanwick. At the next waypoint, which is going to be at position 49 degrees North, 40 degrees West, the position report is transmitted to Gander Oceanic, Shanwick having now safely handed over control of the flight. Control will stay with Gander until 'Foxbat Zero-One' leaves the Oceanic area and enters the domestic airspace at its destination.

On the return journey this process is reversed. Position reports will be passed to Gander Oceanic until the aircraft arrives at 30 degrees West, where that report is passed to both Gander and Shanwick, before Gander hands-off to Shanwick. At either end of the journey, once the aircraft has left Oceanic airspace and rejoined domestic ATC, it becomes subject to the usual requirements of controlled airpsace etc.

Concorde

Because of its incredible speed differential to other aircraft, and the considerable cost of the aviation jet fuel it burns, Concorde needs and gets special conditions. Speedbird-Concorde as all British Airways Concorde's are called, is restricted to subsonic flight while within the London FIR/UIR. ATC tries to give Concorde 'straight-out, continuous climb'; 'straight-in, continuous descent' arrangements to conserve fuel, what's known as Concorde's Cruise-Climb Profile.

Concorde's fuel calculations are critical, with every stage of the flight carefully worked out. So much fuel is allowed for movement on the taxiway; if that fuel isn't used then the engines have to be run until it is. If it begins to look like it's going to burn more fuel on taxying than was allowed for, queues will be jumped to get the Speedbird into the air. To save Concorde making any large changes of heading on the climb-out (after take-off), Concorde always uses runways 27R / 27L at Heathrow, which both face West – the direction in which it needs to fly.

After take-off, Concorde climbs swiftly to around 28,000 feet, travelling at Mach .95! This speed can cause problems for ATC, who have to shift other traffic out of its way very smartly. The aim is to give Concorde a continuous climb to cruise level. Usually, aircraft are climbed in stages up to cruise level, maintaining various altitudes until the next level is clear. As Speedbird-Concorde begins the climb to cruise and supersonic flight, the captain applies *re-heat* to the engines, which sends the fuel used figures through the roof! Any deviation ordered by ATC at this critical stage would punch huge holes in Concorde's fuel budget!

South of Swansea, in the Bristol Channel, Concorde powers up to go supersonic, with full re-heat on. At its normal cruise level of 60,000 feet it will fly at Mach 2, or twice the speed of sound, completing the Heathrow–New York run in fifty per cent of the time taken by a subsonic jetliner.

Much the same system is used on Concorde's return journey. A straight-in, constant descent profile is aimed for, which means a gentle descent out in the Western Approaches, terminating on the runway at the airport. Normally, Heathrow is a busy airport, with aircraft arriving at the four Standard Terminal Arrival Routes – Ockham, Biggin, Bovingdon and Lambourne, and 'holding' there. Again. Concorde cannot 'hold' because of the enormous amount of fuel this would require. As it leaves oceanic airspace it receives information about the current state of Heathrow arrivals. If there's going to be problems, then Concorde throttles back, or even orbits subsonically; anything rather than hold!

Speedbird Sunburn!

Cruising at an altitude of 60,000 feet does have its problems, one of which is, that if it's not careful, Speedbird-Concorde can be severely sunburned! Emissions from the sun, carried earthwards in the solar wind, such as the effects of active prominences and flares on the sun's photosphere, can raise radiation at 60,000 feet to dangerous levels, especially around the peak of a sunspot cycle, such as the just-passed peak of Cycle-22. Concorde has a system of radiation monitors along its fuselage which constantly monitor ambient radiation levels, and when they rise too high, Concorde transmits an 'RCL' to Shanwick Aeradio for permission to descend to 45,000 feet.

Oceanic Concorde

At 8 degrees West longitude, ATC control of Speedbird-Concorde passes from LATCC at West Drayton to Shanwick Clearance on 127.650. Note that, as Concorde flies mostly above weather systems, it doesn't use the North Atlantic Organised Track system, it has a special track of its own. The two permanent North Atlantic Tracks assigned to Concorde are Tracks Sierra-Mike (westbound crossing) and Sierra-November (eastbound crossing). There is a third permanent track used when conditions are impossible on either 'Mike, or 'November; Track Sierra-Oscar.

Concorde's call to Shanwick Delivery is more in the way of a courtesy. As its North Atlantic Tracks are permanently assigned, there's no need to ask for permission to use them. The captain relays the position at which his aircraft entered the Ocean Control Area, and lists the waypoints he will use to report progress. There is a small database of Concorde's airband radio frequencies in the Radiodatabase section.

So You Think YOU Could Be An Air Traffic Controller?

How would you rate *your* potential as an ATC Officer? There is a way to find out. There is available a superb ATC simulator for various home computers called Heathrow Air Traffic Control. And this is most definitely *not* a computer game!

You are presented with a screen which shows you the Heathrow Approach Controller's Secondary Surveillance Radar Screen, the four VOR arrival beacons and a graphic image of Heathrow's twin runways. The idea is that you have to pass R/T messages to various aircraft circling the VOR beacons (by typing-in each instruction), give them a heading to steer, a speed and an altitude, line them up with the ILS and bring them safely into land.

At first, you'll find yourself frantically sending the aircraft all over the skies – this is a very, very real simulation! All aspects of approach control are covered, including minimum altitudes, aircraft separation, minimum/maximum airspeeds, and wake-turbulence. Just like in the real world, there is a delay between ordering an aircraft down to a certain flight level and the aircraft actually arriving at that level. I thoroughly recommend this program. So far, I've written-off millions of pounds' worth of aircraft!

Contact Hewson Consultants Limited, 56B Milton Trading Estate, Milton, Abingdon Oxford. Telephone 0235 832939. My version is designed for the Amstrad PCW 8256/8512 computers, but I have seen this program working on the BBC series computers and various Commodore machines. Hewson's will give you full details.

Part 4
The Plane Spotter

This is the part of the Handbook which explains what plane spotters actually get up to, and what use they make of their airband radio receivers, binoculars, telescopes, cameras, maps, charts and flight schedules.

Understanding ATC Radiotelephony (R/T)

So far we've only examined Air Traffic Control (ATC) messages in the context of controller/pilot transmissons. It's time we delved a little deeper into ATC's use of radio, looking firstly at the phonetic alphabet which is used constantly on airband radio by ATCOs and pilots.

ATC RADIOTELEPHONY TERMINOLOGY

The ICAO Phonetic Alphabet

A	Alpha	AL-FA	B	Bravo	BRA-VOH
C	Charlie	CHAR-LEY	D	Delta	DEL-TAH
E	Echo	EKO	F	Foxtrot	FOCKS-TROT
G	Golf	GOLF	H	Hotel	HO-TEL
I	India	IN-DE-YA	J	Juliet	JEW-LEE-ET
K	Kilo	KEY-LOW	L	Lima	LEE-MAH
M	Mike	MIKE	N	November	NO-VEM-BUR
O	Oscar	OS-KAR	P	Papa	PAH-PAH
Q	Quebec	KWEE-BEK	R	Romeo	RO-ME-OH
S	Sierra	SEE-AIR-RAH	T	Tango	TANGO
U	Uniform	YOO-NEE-FORM	V	Victor	VIK-TOR
W	Whiskey	WISS-KEY	X	X-Ray	ECKS-RAY
Y	Yankee	YAN-KEE	Z	Zulu	ZOO-LOO

EXAMPLE   Aeroplane Callsign GFMDQ becomes:
Golf-Foxtrot-Mike-Delta-Quebec. Or:
GOLF FOCKS-TROT MIKE DEL-TA KWEE-BEK.

And The Numbers

0	Zero	ZEAR-OH	1	One	WUN
2	Two	TOO	3	Three	TREE
4	Four	FOW-ER	5	Five	FIFE
6	Six	SIX	7	Seven	SEV-VUN
8	Eight	AIT	9	Nine	NINER

1,000 = TOW-SAND ('TOW' as in 'HOW')

EXAMPLE   QNH 1018:
               'QNH – Wun Zear-oh Wun AIT.'
               Turn-right, heading 270:
               'Turn-right onto heading Too Sev-vun Zero.'
               Cumulous cloud, 3,000 feet:
               'Cumulous cloud, Tree-Zero-Zero-Zero feet' Or:
               'Cumulous cloud, Tree Tow-sand feet.'

There are some standard ATC R/T phrases. The most common ones, which may be heard in any airport/En-route context, are:

ACKNOWLEDGE	Confirm reception of message AND understanding
AFFIRMATIVE	Yes
APPROVED	Permission granted for the proposed action(s)
CANCEL	Annul previous (or specified) instruction(s)
CAUTION	Beware of (the following conditions/situation)
CHECK	Confirm to your own satisfaction
CLEARED	Permission to proceed under the specified conditions
CONFIRM	Reception/transmission of a message, speed, level, heading
CONTACT	Call the (named) service on (radio frequency), new form for the old 'QSY' – (change frequency)
CORRECT	Right, yes, affirmative, OKAY
CORRECTION	Error in the last R/T message, the correct version is –
DISREGARD	Forget that last transmission, or specified part of it
NEGATIVE	No, permission *not* granted, do not proceed
MONITOR	Listen out on (radio frequency) for . . .
PASS MESSAGE	Transmit details, request, invitation to transmit
READ BACK	Repeat the last message (or specified part) back to me also, message-category on HF airband
REPORT	Supply the information requested. *Note!* the response may *not* be immediate, as in 'Report passing . . .' etc
REQUEST	Please supply, obtain, I want to know
SAY AGAIN	What? repeat last message, your R/T NOT clear/good
STANDBY	Station calling, please wait; station already in

	contact please wait; *neither* station to assume any onwards or upwards clearance
VERIFY	Please check AND confirm the following . . .

In addition there are some phrases which are exclusive to R/T, such as:
HOW DO YOU READ?

Readability (of R/T signals) is measured on a scale of between 1 and 5. 'Strength 5' is an extremely strong radio signal. 'Strength 1' is virtually unreadable. Everything in between being pro rata.

I SAY AGAIN.

I am repeating this message (or part of) for added emphasis, because of its importance, or due to bad R/T conditions.

And finally, the procedural R/T messages which keep both sides informed over whose turn it is to transmit, and who's to listen.

OVER.

I have finished speaking and require an answer from you. (Rarely heard now.)

OUT.

I have finished speaking, I have said everything and I am now going to stop transmitting. No answer is required from you. (Rarely heard now.)

ROGER

I have received your last radio transmission completely. *Note!* ROGER should *never* be used as a reply to a direct 'YES/NO' type question.

WILCO

I have received your last instructions and I will comply with them. Short form of WILl COmply

The use of *over* and *out* at the end of R/T transmissions is virtually obsolete; except for pilots with a very new and shiny Private Pilots Licence! The end of each R/T message is apparent due to the content of what's been said, or that the pilot/controller has stopped speaking! Due to the rigid format of ATC radio telephony, both sides know what information is to be passed and when a response is needed. You'll quickly adapt to this.

Callsigns

ATC units are often talking to many aircraft, often at the same time. They need to be able to identify quickly and unambiguously exactly who they're in contact with. R/T Callsigns are used for this purpose.

Light Aircraft

Light aircraft callsigns are quite straightforward. They consist of five letters always starting with 'G', which is the international country identifier for the UK – so *all* British aircraft start with this letter, and four other letters. For example: G-BCRT.

On initial contact with an ATC service, a light aircraft will give its *full* callsign phonetically, e.g. 'Golf-Bravo-Charlie-Romeo-Tango'. After this first contact (and assuming that the aircraft's still talking to the same ATC unit) it is customary to abbreviate the callsign to the first, fourth and fifth letters only such as: 'Golf-Romeo-Tango'. Although this is often further chopped to: 'Romeo-Tango'. Unless, of course, there is another aircraft with the same last two letters, in which case the *full* call is used *all* of the time.

Commercial Aircraft

Airline companies' callsigns are also fairly simple. They usually take the form of the airline company's name *and* a number – more of which in a moment. For example:

QANTAS – Qantas Airlines.
AEROFLOT – Aeroflot.
AIR EUROPE – Air Europe.

Some airline companies' callsigns are *not* so apparent; such as British Airway's SPEEDBIRD; PAN AMerican's CLIPPER or sometimes CLIPPER-JET, and Aer Lingus' SHAMROCK.

Flight Numbers

As well as the callsign, various combinations of numbers and letters are used as the flight number. To airband radio listeners, these commercial aircraft callsigns and flight numbers are invaluable as they tell us much of what we like to know. The callsign tells us the airline company, and the flight number indirectly identifies the aircraft type *and* where it's going to or coming from.

Most scheduled airline services retain the same combination of callsign and flight number for years, and familiarity with certain airways reporting points will soon show you the 'regulars'. Many companies use consecutive flight numbers for flights outbound and inbound, or suffix the flight number with the letters 'A' or 'B' for the same purpose. For example, the British Midland Airways seven-days-a-week Advanced Turbo Prop (ATP) shuttle service between East Midland and Heathrow airports.

Flight 'BD224' is the 1100 shuttle from Heathrow, arriving East Midland at 1150 GMT.

Flight 'BD225' is the return shuttle, departing East Midland at 1235, arriving Heathrow at 1325 GMT.

On hearing ATC talking to 'Midland 224', or the pilot talking to ATC 'Flight BD225 . . .'; it's not apparent what type of aircraft 'BD224/5' is, nor where it's going to or coming from. The airband listener at the airport doesn't know if it's going to land, or simply overfly. That's why I said flight numbers supply airband listeners with indirect information. To get the aircraft type, its destination etc. you'll have to look it up in a guide, such as an airport timetable, or one of the books available to the plane spotter, such as *Flight Routings 1990*, by T.T. Williams (see Bibliography, Appendix 3).

Where to Listen

Where you listen to airband radio messages is important. For example, there wouldn't be much point in trying to receive ATC messages from Glasgow Airport if you lived in Suffolk. And then taking your airband receiver back to the shop for a refund because you can't! Be realistic about what you want to monitor.

The Airport

Armed with your airband radio receiver, aircraft recognition, flight routings and, of course! a copy of this Handbook (which supplies you with airport ATC frequencies) plus binoculars, you're ready for a visit to the airport. The number of airport ATC personnel depends on the size of the terminal. Each controller has his or her own working frequency. Assuming your airband receiver has memories and some method of scanning them, there is a way to listen to *all* the airport ATC frequencies in use, virtually at the same time.

Using Memory Search

A lot depends on how the memories in your receiver are organized. Some radios have just ten memories: others have a hundred or so, arranged in various banks. For example, my SIGNAL R532 has one hundred memories organized in ten banks (A to J) of ten memories (1 to 10). Using your receiver's memory programming feature, enter the required airport ATC frequencies into consecutive memory locations, and LOCK-OUT all the other memories in that bank.

Lock-out is simply a method of telling either a scan or search to ignore whichever memory locations are tagged with the lock-out flag. When the scan or search is started the receiver misses out the memory locations locked-out, saving time.

At the airport, all you need do is to initiate a memory search, and the receiver will scan the various locations you programmed while ignoring those locked-out. Any transmissions from Tower, Approach, Radar, Ground, Delivery etc. will be 'spotted' by the memory search, allowing you to hear just about everything that happens on airport R/T. Of course, should Tower and, say, Ground transmit simultaneously, then the receiver will only 'latch' onto one or the other; usually the first one it captures during the search.

No Lock-Out?

Even if your receiver doesn't have a lock-out, or programmable memory search feature, you can still use this method of listening to airport ATC R/T. My SIGNAL receiver doesn't have lock-out, what I do is this:

In Memories 1, 5 and 8 of Bank 'A', I have the East Midlands Tower – 124.000mHz. In Memories 2, 6 and 9 I have East Midlands Approach – 119.650mHz.

Locations 3, 7 and 10 have East Midlands Radar – 120.125mHz; and finally memory number 4 has the, as yet apparently unused, East Midlands Ground Movement Control frequency of 121.900mHz. This fills up the entire 'A' Bank, and by-passes the need for lock-out.

I could just programme memory locations 1 to 4, leaving 5 to 10 'empty'; but this means that the receiver is wasting time searching 'unoccupied' locations.

If it's going to search them anyway (which it is, because there's no lock-out) then it might just as well be usefully employed, hence the multiple redundancy of frequencies.

The end result is exactly the same as with lock-out; I get to monitor all the airport's ATC frequencies without having to tune the receiver, or indeed touch it at all! Very useful if you're making tape-recordings of ATC transmissions.

Modifications

Broadcast + airband type receivers have a common failing; because they have a tuning scale/pointer arrangement, setting them to a precise frequency is very, very difficult indeed. Sometimes, even the thickness of the dial pointer is enough to mask around 3 to 4 VHF airband channels! Their usefulness is diminished greatly by this lack of tuning accuracy. However, all is not lost – they can be modified (bodged?).

ALBA receiver with Airband, modified for use

The photograph on this page demonstrates the method. A piece of sticky-tape (masking tape is about the best for this purpose) is fixed either to the top or the bottom of the receiver's tuning dial/scale. Where a station is heard *and* definitely identified, a mark is made on the sticky-tape in relation to the position of the dial pointer. This mark has to be a thin one, and you won't have space to write on the name of the station heard due to the limited bandspreading of such receivers. Use either a number or a letter, and write down elsewhere which mark corresponds to what service or station.

Fortunately – or unfortunately, depending on your viewpoint – great accuracy of marking-out isn't necessary. Although the average VHF airband R/T signal is around 10kHz wide, the filters on this type of receiver are considerably wider than this, so close enough is good enough. The fun starts when you're trying to listen to Heathrow Departures GMC (121.700mHz), Departures ATIS (121.750mHz) or Heathrow Tower on 121.000mHz. And getting them all at the same time!

Spectating

Finally, remember that at some airports you'll be spectating under sufferance; even though you bring in much needed revenue! Remember the *Plane Spotters' Code* as given in the Introduction.

THE AIRWAYS PLANE SPOTTER

I have a few friends who cannot get to an airport, consequently they do most of their listening from home. If you live under an airway, reporting point, or within one of the Terminal Manoeuvering Areas (TMA) then you'll be fortunate enough to hear many En-route ATC R/T messages. How can you discover if you live near any of these areas? Simple. You need to acquire an airways chart, such as British Airways Aerad Low Altitude EFF, EUR 1/2. The illustration on page 138 shows a section of this chart concerning Airway Bravo 1, which I'm about to discuss. Airways charts may be obtained from the addresses listed in Appendix 7, used or out-of-date charts cost around £3 each (depending on source).

Having acquired your airways chart, roughly locate your home area on it and put a mark. Now look for the nearest airway, or airways, which are marked at various points with VOR/DME combinations, reporting points and NDB beacons (gained from the charts *Legend* booklet). On airways charts, beacons and reporting points have their latitude and longitude printed alongside their positions, and it is a simple matter to transfer these bearings onto an O/S map to locate these navaids etc. accurately, in relation to your home. But do remember, the latitudes and longitudes given are in degrees and decimal minutes.

For example, where I live, Airway Bravo 1, which runs virtually east/west across England, from around Hull on the East coast to the Wirral on the West, is 12 nautical miles north of my home. Bravo 4 is 20 nautical miles to my south/west. The RAF Finningley NDB FY on 408.5kHz is 7 nautical miles to my north-north/east, and the Gamston VOR/DME is also 7 nautical miles south-south/east of my home.

Know Your Frequency

Having established which airways, reporting points and navigation beacons are nearest to you, the next thing you need is a list of airways and their ATC control frequencies: these are listed in Radiodatabase 2 at the back of the Handbook.

Although I'm dealing with airways in my area, the rules and method used to discover this information are exactly the same wherever you live. After locating Airway Bravo 1 on the Aerad chart, I then looked up the Air Traffic Control Centre (ATCC) responsible for control of this airway. In actual fact, due to the limited range of VHF R/T and the high potential workload for a single controller, Airway Bravo 1 is broken up into more manageable sections.

Know Your Area

Working from my Aerad chart, and the list of airways ATC frequencies in Radiodatabase 2, I find that the section of Airway Bravo 1 west of the Wallasey VOR/DME (near Liverpool) above FL155 is controlled by London on a primary frequency of 128.050mHz. (There are secondary frequencies too; but they are irrelevant here.) Below FL155, control is via the sub-centre at Manchester, on a primary of 133.050mHz.

From the Wallasey VOR/DME, on the 086 degree radial, to the BARTN reporting point, (Liverpool to near Manchester) above FL155 control is by London, again on 128.050mHz. Below FL155 Manchester has control on 125.100mHz.

The next section of Bravo 1 is my prime interest, as there are two reporting points which are close to me; DENBY and UPTON (reporting points mostly have five letter names, by the way). From the BARTN reporting point, east to the Ottringham VOR/DME combination, near Hull, London Airways has control above FL155 on 131.050mHz, while below FL155 control is by the Manchester sub-centre, on a frequency of 126.650mHz. East of Ottringham VOR, out over the North Sea, until the handover to European ATC, London has control of Bravo 1 at all flight levels, on a frequency of 134.250mHz.

Selection of various air navigation charts

174

Know Your Charts

I said earlier, when discussing airband radio receiver features, that it wasn't a good idea to initiate a frequency scan and let your radio blindly wander all over the place, in the hope that it might run into something interesting. It is much better to know where the radio signals will be. So it is with airways airband radio listening. Know where the airways, reporting points, VOR/DME combinations and ATC control frequencies are in relation to your home, rather than blindly tune, or scan around on your receiver. An airways chart is the essential item for this type of listening.

The first time you see an airways chart it will seem like a bewildering mass of squiggly lines and strange symbols. To help your understanding, it is essential to ask for a chart legends booklet when ordering a chart, which explains what the various symbols represent. Familiarity with the chart brings understanding, and in no time at all you'll be surprised how much information can be got from one. Not only the locations of VORs, NDBs, reporting points and airways, but also which airband frequencies are used as well.

Airways ATC Reporting Message Format

Aircraft position reports follow the following format.

1	Callsign	'Midland 567.'
2	Position	'Four-three DME from Ottringham.'
3	Time	'At four-five.'
4	Flight Level	'Flight level two-two-zero.'
5	Next Position	'Next; Denby.'
6	ETA	'At zero-five.'

or, as it comes over the R/T:

AIRCRAFT	'London – Midland 567 is four-three DME from Ottringham at time four-five, en-route Liverpool Speke. Flight level 220 and estimating DENBY at zero-five.'
LATCC	'Roger Midland 567. Maintain flight level 220.'
AIRCRAFT	'Maintain 220 – Midland 567.'
LATCC	'Eckto 23 Alpha. Descend flight level 250.'
AIRCRAFT	'Roger; Eckto 23 Alpha – out of 330 for level 250.'

175

NON-ATC R/T TRANSMISSIONS

Frequency Offsets

Apart from ATC R/T transmissions, there are a few other types of interesting radio traffic. There are the various VOLMET stations whose frequencies you'll find in Appendix 1, and private, company radio messages between an aircraft and its parent company's base airport. When listening to some of these services and in particular VOLMETs, which require more than a single transmitter to cover the amount of country they do, you may have to tune your receiver slightly higher or lower (between 3–5 kHz) in frequency.

This is because if each relay station transmitted on the same frequency, in any area where two or more relay stations' signals overlap it would set up an annoying whistling effect – known as *Hetereodyne Whistle*. To avoid this, each relay station transmits its signal just slightly off the frequency of its nearest neighbour. Where there are two relays their signals are offset some 3kHz – one 3kHz up, the other 3kHz down. Where there are three, the offset is 5kHz and four relays require an offset of 7kHz.

Company Messages

Aircraft need to contact their parent companies to inform them of fuel and victual requirements, tell them of departure/expected arrival times, and to order any special requirements for passengers on arrival, such as wheelchairs, or a nurse. These 'Company Messages' are often quite interesting, and provide a fascinating insight into the passenger/cargo handling side of aviation for those spotters who make a study of airport operations. These transmissions usually take place between 131.400mHz and 131.950mHz. Some company frequencies are listed in Radiodatabase 8. By the way, PAX is airband-speak for passengers, so if you hear something like: '. . . with nine-zero pax on-board.' it means 90 passengers and *not* 90 parcels!

HF Oceanic Airband Listening

Most HF airbands listening will inevitably be carried out from home, due to the enormous size (compared to VHF) of the aerials, and the receiver's mains voltage power requirement. However, some types can be used at airports; indeed I often take such a receiver with me on various jaunts.

AOR AR3000 HF/VHF/UHF communications receiver

The Plot Thickens

Many HF airband listeners like to monitor position reports from aircraft on the North Atlantic Organised Track System and then plot each way-point given onto a globe or an Atlantic chart, following the progress of the flight. Indeed, Concorde may be followed in this way, although, unless you live near to the departing/arriving airports, you won't be able to follow Speedbird-Concorde once it re-enters domestic airspace. Sometimes you will be able to hear the aircraft directly, but as Shanwick repeats position reports back to the pilot, you can still plot them.

Other HF Airband Radio Transmissions

Apart from the position reports and SelCal tests of aircraft crossing the Atlantic, there are other interesting HF airband signals to monitor as well. There are the various VOLMET metereological reporting stations from around the world, and company transmissions. VOLMET stations broadcast aviation weather reports for various airports around the world. Their content, frequencies and schedules are listed in Appendix 1.

Company Transmissions

It is often necessary for an aircraft on the North Atlantic run to communicate directly with its company's office. Information such as the actual time of departure, estimated time of arrival, fuel and victual requirements, engineering information, and any special passenger needs such as wheelchairs etc. are passed directly from the aircraft back to its base airport. British Airways run their own company HF R/T link, often handling radio traffic for other airline companies as well as their own.

Most airline companies find maintaining their own HF radio facility too expensive, and use third party facilities, such as ARINC, or one of the national telecommunications agencies, such as British Telecom's Portishead Radio, which provides direct radio telephone links between an aircraft and its parent company.

THE SPECIALIST PLANE SPOTTER

Aviation is such a huge subject that no-one can really hope to become an expert in every aspect. What tends to happen with enthusiasts is, after the initial burst of enthusiasm and thirst for knowledge has subsided, they pursue one or two aspects which interest them the most. Not to the exclusion of everything else, of course, it's just that their main energies are channelled into their favourite aviation subjects.

For example, although I want to know about any mechanical device which takes to the air, my particular interests are: airband radio listening, Oceanic Air Traffic Control and spacecraft such as the various communications and metereological satellites. To finish this section on The Plane Spotter, I am listing the major enthusiasts areas of specialisation together with short notes about them, in the hope that I might list something you'd like to know more about, or even give you some new ideas.

Hunt The Beacon!

This is often a very pleasant way of spending a day, and also draws on other skills you may have (or need to acquire) to be successful. Apart from getting you out into the fresh air! The 'rules of the game' are: first you have to actually hear *and* make a tape recording of the beacon in question (not all that easy!). Then you locate the exact position of the NDB or VOR/DME installation (using Airways/Ordnance Survey charts), visit the site and take a photograph of it. Believe me, it's not as simple as I've made it sound!

I receive the RAF Finningley NDB beacon – FY at strength 5 (very loud). It's easily identified, by the way, from its callsign sent in (very) slow Morse code, which sounds exactly like: Di-Di-Dah-Dit Dah-Di-Dah-Dah: or put another way; Dot-Dot-Dash-Dot, Dash-Dot-Dash-Dash. Many of the names of various navaids are only approximately geographically correct, although their listing of latitude and longitude on an airways chart is, of course very accurate.

First you acquire the latitude/longitude of the installation you're seeking from the appropriate airways chart, and then transfer it to a suitable map, such as an Ordnance Survey Landranger series. Having found the exact location, off you go to take the photograph, bearing in mind that the installation may well be on private land, so ensure that the country code is observed at all times, and that permission to enter or cross private land is obtained before entry.

SelCal Codes And Aircraft Registrations

Many plane spotters collect aircraft registration numbers and letters, much like other people collect train numbers. There are books available (see Bibliography) which list aircraft registrations and inform you of the aircraft type and its present owner. Sometimes aircraft have names, as well as their international registration. For example; the British Midland Airways, Douglas DC9-15, G-BMAG is a familiar sight flying in and out of East Midlands International. It also carries the name of *The Nassau Diamond*.

Many plane spotters also collect SelCal codes. As these codes are registered to a particular aircraft and tend to stay with it, even if it's leased or sold, they often provide a link between the present or the previous registration. Books listing SelCal codes are listed in Appendix 3.

ATC Operations

Studying air traffic control can be a lifetime's work in itself! Listening via airband radio will teach you much. Books, airport and air traffic control centre visits can all help fill in the missing gaps. Of course, you can't simply march into the airport's control tower and demand a quick look-see. What you can do is to join one of the aviation societies who arrange a whole series of visits to airports and ATCCs in this country and abroad, as well as supplying invaluable 'behind the scenes' information to their members. In fact, next to an airband radio receiver and an airways chart (or two), the very next thing to spend your money on is a year's membership of an aviation society. I can promise you that you'll never regret one penny of the money expended.

Airband Radio Listening

Although I've already provided what appears to be a huge amount of information on this subject, you'd be amazed at what I've had to leave out! This is one of those subjects which allows you to study others in more detail, such as air traffic control, airport operations etc. The initial purchase price of suitable equipment may seem high, but then it's a non-recurring expense. Once you have it, then it's yours for life, and will provide hours of entertainment, education and sheer pleasure. Put that against four or five pints of beer in the local pub, three times a week. Given a year, you will have totally recouped the purchase price.

What's more, only the 'bottom end' of the airband receiver market holds little resale value. Buying good gear from the start ensures a very respectable trade-in, or sell price should you ever decide to upgrade, or change direction in the future. Don't forget to make tape recordings of ATC R/T, they help enormously when trying to understand something which at first sight appears difficult.

Photography

Again, like airband radio, photography often provides the means to make a study of another area. I've only given very basic information about the subject within the Handbook, but speaking as an ex-professional photographer, it's well worth your while learning as much as you can, especially processing your own colour transparencies (slides) which, believe me, is now a very, very simple process. Only by doing your own processing can you really learn the art of photography.

As an added incentive, and to subsidise your own picture-taking, there is an almost insatiable thirst for aircraft transparencies and monochrome prints, by the aeronautical press, various picture agencies, books and magazines. But they must be of the highest possible quality – correctly exposed and processed, and with no vital parts missing! The best composed photograph in the world isn't any good to anyone if you can't see half of the aircraft due to incorrect exposure or poor processing!

Airline Companies And Livery

Photography is the ideal tool for the study of the often fascinating colour schemes of various airlines. Indeed, aircraft 'Tailplane Art' – company designs on the aircraft's tail fin – are often exquisitely drawn and coloured and make beautiful colour posters. Such photos often provide many an enjoyable lecture or quiz at the aviation society's meetings, such as 'from the tailplane, name the company'; and if you're into this subject, you could well find yourself a very popular person with your club chairman!

Aircraft

They call it Twitching in bird-watching circles. That's when a rare bird has been sighted, and amateur ornithologists from all over the country descend upon the place where the rarity has been seen. It's the same thing with plane spotters who specialise in aircraft types. I've met spotters who've travelled hundreds of miles to see a particular aircraft, once 'the word' had been spread along the grapevine. Of course, both photography and an airband receiver are invaluable tools for this specialisation. As is up-to-date information and specifications of aircraft types.

Studying and photographing aircraft types requires a lot of background information, as often the differences between variations of the same type are very difficult to see. But then, to someone who knows what they're looking for, this is what makes the visit worthwhile. And, getting close enough for a detailed photo is difficult too, especially with the increased amount of security at most airports. But then, if it was easy, everyone would be doing it!

OTHER INTERESTING PLACES FOR THE PLANE SPOTTER TO VISIT

Of course, airports aren't the only places where you will find aircraft. There are many airfields scattered around the country, and they are much more numerous than international airports, so there is every chance that you'll find one close to where you live. Airfields are usually very friendly places where the pilots and staff are very willing to chat to the genuine enthusiast. See the photograph on p182, Carlos chatting to the Captain of a Beechcraft Turboprop, prior to take-off.

Airfields

Airfields vary greatly in their range of sophistication. Some are a scattered collection of wooden huts and a grass runway: others have a tarmac surface, taxiway systems, a purpose-built control tower and passenger terminal, and often a part-time customs service. There are a few important differences between an airfield and an international airport. For example, an airport will have a CAA-licensed team of air traffic control officers (ATCOs) whose instructions carry the weight of civil law behind them. At an airfield there aren't usually any ATCOs; they tend to have an Airfield Controller instead. He or she must have

Carlos talking to a pilot at Gamston Airfield

a Certificate of Competence, which is issued by the CAA after a simple test.

Airfield Controller

The Airfield Controller cannot give instructions to pilots, such as those issued by a trained and CAA-licensed ATCO. Instead they are only allowed to give advice and information, prefixing messages to pilots with the phrase at your discretion, or in other words, on your head be it! Airfields are issued with a VHF airband frequency, commonly prefixed with 'A/G', meaning Air-To-Ground. The airfield will often use its name followed by the words Radio or Information as their R/T callsign. For example: 'Netherthorpe Radio'; or 'Netherthorpe Information'. The acronym AFIS – Air-Field Information Service – is sometimes used as well, such as 'Netherthorpe AFIS', or 'Gamston AFIS'.

Netherthorpe airfield. Nottinghamshire

Mainly private, light aircraft, such as flying schools and clubs use the airfields around the country, and they often hold special events throughout the year where some exotic aircraft may fly in for the weekend. There are also other types of visitors, especially throughout the long summer evenings, where pleasure pilots of microlights, biplanes, and even the odd glider have been known to drop in at my local airfield.

Gliding

There's something intrinsically right about a glider, or sailplane aircraft, as it sweeps silently across the skies. Most glider flying in this country is done at club level, and there's almost certainly one near where you live. Gliding appeals to all age groups, and is more of a group activity than powered aircraft flying. Glider pilots earn certificates of competence, working from the British Gliding Association's syllabus. Watching the sailplanes doing circuits and bumps around the local gliding club's airfield is a relaxing way to spend a summer's evening, but don't get too close. In no time at all you may find yourself roped in to help, such as wheeling aircraft out of the hangars, or steadying the wings as the sailplane starts its take-off run.

Gliders are launched either by a tow-rope and winch assembly, or by a powered aeroplane acting as a tug. You can monitor the sailplanes on their National Frequency allocations, which are: 130.100, 130.125 and

130.400mHz. You may hear a student glider pilot talking back to his instructor on the ground, listen to a pilot talking to the winch-operator when ready to drop the tow rope, or monitor a sailplane flying in from a distant gliding airfield, on a training flight for a higher certificate of competence. Glider flying is great fun and relatively cheap. Often a syndicate is formed, with several people owning a part-share in an aircraft. As I said earlier, don't stand around looking like you know what you're doing or you'll end up as a club member, and hooked on glider flying!

Hot Air Ballooning

The sight of a multi-coloured, giant balloon envelope made from rip-stop nylon ghosting along in the evening breeze is quite stirring. I well remember attending the John Player Hot Air Balloon World Championships in the late seventies, as a photographer, and suffering from terminal ecstasy as around 60 hot air balloons rose almost silently through the early morning autumn mist at Rufford Abbey in Nottinghamshire. The beauty and, conversely, the problem with ballooning is that they don't need an airfield or runway for launching, so finding out where ballooning takes place can be a problem. However, the British Balloon and Airship Club will be only too willing to provide this information.

Hot air balloon pilots have to obtain a special version of the Private Pilots Licence, and when trained they must undertake a test flight with a CAA examiner. Once they've successfully completed their test flight, they are licensed as a qualified hot air balloon pilot. Monitoring the progress of a balloon through the air can be very interesting and often quite hilarious too!

The frequency allocated to balloons is 129.900mHz. The radio traffic mainly concerns the pilot of the balloon keeping in radio contact with the ground recovery team, who travel by vehicle on the roads. The fun starts when either the pilot or the recovery team gets lost! I have heard some hot air balloon pilots keeping in radio contact with the ground recovery team via Citizen Band radio, so it's often worth while keeping an ear on the CB, assuming you have one, of course!

Hang-Gliders

Like glider flying, hang-gliders earn certificates of competence through their national society, although the actual rules governing hang-gliding are few; which is one of the main attractions of this sport, its relative freedom from red tape and regulations. Like ballooning, it's not always easy to find out where the hang-gliders hang out, if you'll pardon the dreadful pun! The National Hang-Glider frequency is 129.900mHz, and R/T traffic is mostly between pupil–pilot and a ground instructor, although there are several hang-gliding competitions throughout the year, and R/T traffic increases considerably during these events.

In a hang-gliding competition, pilots are given a course to fly, passing over a set number of waypoints. In some cases, marshalls are located at each waypoint and radio back the registration number of the aircraft passing them. Sometimes a camera is strapped to the airframe of the hang-glider, and the pilot has to take a photograph of the waypoint as it is overflown. Whichever system is used, it all makes for interesting listening.

OPTICAL EQUIPMENT

Being without some form of optical aid at an airport is to be disadvantaged, especially if you're going to be collecting aircraft registrations. Due to the increased security at most airports it's very difficult to get close to the aircraft. Basically, there are two types of optical aid you can use – binoculars and telescopes. Both have their advantages and disadvantages. As in all things, it depends on what you want to do with them.

Binoculars

Prismatic binoculars are the type most people purchase, although there are other types as well and I'll be looking at them in moment. There are two sets of numbers which accompany a pair of binoculars, and they tell you how suitable they will be for a particular purpose. Typical of such numbers are: 10×50, 7×50, or 8×40. The first numbers – 10, 7 and 8 – tell you by how many times the binoculars magnify. The second number, 50, 50 and 40 refer to the diameter of the object glasses i.e. the lenses at the front. The bigger this number then the more light will be collected by the binocular lenses.

All optical aids have two basic functions: to collect light, and then to magnify it. Which of the two numbers on binoculars is most important depends entirely on what you want to do with them. For example, an amateur astronomer would want to gather the maximum amount of light, so would be looking for at least 7×50 binoculars, which give an exit pupil of 7mm. Exit pupil is the amount of light leaving the binoculars' eyepieces, and entering the eye. The larger it is, then the more light enters the eye and the more you can see: anything over 8mm will be wasted as the maximum dilation of the human eye pupil is around this size. So 5×50 binoculars are wasted.

At the airport, where there's usually plenty of light around, the plane spotter is more likely to be interested in the first number, the magnification factor. Bearing in mind exit pupil there's a rough formula for working out the maximum amount of magnification binoculars or telescopes will stand. It is, 10 times magnification for every inch (25mm) of object glass diameter. A fairly average pair of binoculars are 10×50; i.e. ten times magnification and object glasses 50 mm (2 inches) in diameter. This gives an exit pupil of 5mm, which is adequate in normal lighting. You can occasionally find binoculars advertised as 25×50s. Our 'rule-of-thumb' would suggest that this is acceptable, but you work out the exit pupil. (Divide magnification factor into O/G diameter.)

Types Of Binoculars

The most usual type are the Prismatic binoculars, which gives them their distinctive shape. The light-path is folded by passing it through prisms, which increase the focal length, and make magnifications of times 10 quite easy. Occasionally, you may see adverts in newspapers for Gallilean binoculars. This type do not have prisms, so magnification is nearly always limited to around 5 or 6 times.

The latest generation of binoculars are known as Roof Prisms. At first sight they look like Gallilean binoculars, but the prisms are specially carved, flat types which are concealed within the 'bridge', the housing which connects both binocular tubes together. They range in specification from 10×25 up to around 10×60, and are very light-weight.

Because most lenses today are now computer-designed, carved and polished, current binoculars offer astonishing performance at ridiculously low prices. The performance of a pair of 10×50 binoculars today, costing £30 would have cost you at least £200 fifteen years ago, nor would they have been as good as today's! But, beware of the plastic lens! Many cheap binoculars – often from Asia – are made from acrylic material. View them side-by-side with glass lenses, and make your own mind up!

Telescopes

If you're collecting aircraft registration letters, then you may find that a telescope is better suited for your purpose. Generally, they allow a greater range of magnification than binoculars, and often have a zoom eyepiece, which offers a range of continuously adjustable magnifications, from something like ten times, up to sixty. Make sure though that you're not buying an astronomical telescope, where the image is upside down and reversed right-to-left!

The bird-watching magazines carry lots of advertisements for telescopes, and this type is ideal for the plane spotter as the needs of the ornithologist exactly parallel those of the plane spotter.

Types And Costs

Generally, telescopes do cost more than binoculars, although I'm never quite sure why! Having made many telescopes myself, I can't understand why they often cost two to three times more than a good pair of binoculars. It is usual to purchase the telescope without an eyepiece, and then select the eyepiece separately, choosing the magnification to suit. Things to look out for are: a tripod mounting bush – telescopes are difficult to hand hold – a recessed front lens with a hood to stop flare on the object glass, and to protect it from scratching and damage. An average price for a 25×60 – 25 times magnification by 60mm object lens, is around £200.

Binoculars Vs Telescopes

There is no doubt that binoculars are much easier to handle than a telescope, but then, ultimately the telescope will show you more than binoculars. Many people have difficulty holding a telescope, and viewing through one eye. What happens is that they tend to screw-up the eye they're *not* using, which quickly causes strain. Developing the knack of looking through the telescope while still keeping the other eye open is not too difficult, and once mastered makes using a telescope almost as easy as binoculars.

Normally, a tripod is needed for prolonged telescope viewing as your arms quickly tire. In fact, a tripod is also a good idea for binoculars as well, and many photographic/optical shops actually sell special tripod clamps for binoculars (see the photograph on p188). As you'll be needing a tripod for photography as well, buying one would be an excellent idea all round!

Photography

At an airport almost any camera will do, but for consistent results, and for adaptability to any task or situation, the Single Lens Reflex (SLR) camera system cannot be beaten. A basic 35mm or 60×60mm (120) SLR system would comprise of a camera body, standard lens (40mm for 35mm SLRs, 70mm for 60×60mm SLRs), a wide-angle lens (28–35mm for 35mm SLR – 40–60mm for 60×60mm SLRs) and a medium long-focus (telephoto) (200mm for 35mm SLRs – 300mm for 60×60mm SLRs). Of course, nowadays there are various zoom lenses available for

Binocular/Tripod mounting bracket

either SLR format. I consider a tripod an essential part of my camera system, and would be quite lost without it.

Exposure is often difficult, especially when taking pictures of jetliners up in the sky. The TTL (Through-The-Lens) metering system's reading is inflated by the large expanse of bright sky. Spot metering is a partial answer, although it's often difficult to obtain the reading with the aircraft moving so fast. I simply use a handheld meter, and take an ambient meter reading off the back of my hand, and then bracket by taking shots one stop up/down from this mean reading. Black and white film does have considerable exposure latitude, especially if you process your own negatives, so any slight exposure errors will not matter.

Colour transparency film doesn't have the same exposure latitude as monochrome film, but if you bracket exposures thoughtfully, you will have at least one shot absolutely right. Processing your own slides is a must. All you need is a developing tank, average cost around £12 and the relevant chemicals. Later you might want to add a mounting jig etc. One word of warning: if you're going to submit your slides to various publications, *never* mount your slides in glass! Always use the glassless, plastic frames, and clearly label each slide with the title and your name and address.

If you can afford it, a second camera body is a good investment, allowing you to have black and white film in the second camera body while using colour slide film in the other. This way you can obtain a colour and a monochrome photograph of the same subject simply by swapping the lens.

Part 5

Radiodatabases and Airband Frequency Selectors

RADIODATABASE 1. UK AIRPORT ATC FREQUENCIES

ABERDEEN
Approach & Radar	120.400	ATIS	121.850
Emergency GMC	121.600*	GMC	121.700
Radar	120.400	Radar	121.250
Radar	128.300	Tower	118.100

* Common airport Fire etc. emergency frequency

BEDFORD
Approach	124.400	Radar	130.700
Radar	118.375	Tower	130.000

BELFAST ALDERGROVE
Approach	120.000	Emergency GMC	121.600
GMC	121.750	Radar	120.900
Tower	118.300		

BELFAST HARBOUR
Approach	122.450	Tower	130.750

BENBECULA
Approach & Tower	119.200

BIRMINGHAM
Approach	131.325	ATIS	120.725
GMC	121.800	Radar	118.050
Radar	120.500	Tower	118.300

BLACKPOOL
Approach	135.950	Radar	119.950
Tower	118.400		

BOURNEMOUTH (HURN)
Approach	119.625	ATIS	121.950
Departures	121.950	Radar	118.650
Radar	119.750	Tower	125.600

BRISTOL LULSGATE
Approach	132.400	Radar	124.350
Tower	133.850		

CAMBRIDGE
Approach	123.600	Tower	122.200

CARDIFF
Approach	125.850	Radar	120.050
Radar	125.850	Tower	121.200

CARLISLE
Approach & Tower	123.600

CORK
Approach	119.900	Radar	118.800
GMC	121.700	Tower	119.300

COVENTRY
Approach & Tower	119.250	Radar	122.000

DUBLIN
Approach	121.100	Zone Radar [1]	124.650
Zone Radar [2]	128.000	ATIS	118.250
GMC	121.800	Radar	128.000
Radar	118.500	Radar	119.550
Tower	118.600		

DUNDEE
Approach & Tower	122.900

EAST MIDLANDS
Approach & Radar	119.650	Radar	120.125
GMC*	121.900	Tower	124.000

* Not apparently in use, yet

EDINBURGH
Approach	122.550	Radar	118.825
Radar	122.550	Tower	124.325

EXETER
Approach & Radar	128.150	Radar	119.050
Tower	119.800		

GLASGOW
Approach	119.100	Arrivals/Departures	115.400
ATIS	113.400	Radar	119.300
Radar	119.700	Radar	121.300
GMC	121.700	Tower	118.800

GLOUCESTER
Approach & Tower	125.650	Radar	122.900

GUERNSEY
Approach	128.650	ATIS	109.400
Radar	118.900	Radar	124.500
Tower	119.950	GMC	121.800

HATFIELD
Approach	123.350	Radar	119.300
Radar	123.350	Tower	130.800

HAWARDEN
Approach	123.350	Radar	129.850
Tower	124.950		

193

HUMBERSIDE

Approach	123.150	Tower	118.550

INVERNESS

Approach	122.600	Tower	122.600

IPSWICH

Approach & Tower	118.325

ISLE OF MAN

Approach	120.850	Radar	118.200
Radar	120.850	Zone Radar	125.300
Tower	118.900		

JERSEY

Approach	120.300	ATIS	112.200
Radar	118.550	Radar	120.300
Zone Radar	120.450	Zone Radar	125.200
GMC	121.900	Tower	119.450

LEAVESDEN

Approach & Tower	122.150	Radar	121.400

LEEDS/BRADFORD

Approach	123.750	Radar	121.050
Tower	120.300		

LIVERPOOL

Approach & Radar	119.850	Radar	118.450
Tower	118.100		

LONDON (CITY)

Approach	132.700	Radar	128.025
Tower [1]	119.425	Tower [2]	121.775

LONDON HELIPORT

Approach	119.200	Radar	119.900
Tower	122.900		

LONDON GATWICK

Approach	125.875	Clearance Delivery	121.950
Arrivals ATIS	128.475	Departures ATIS	121.750
Radar	118.600	Radar	119.600
Radar	125.875	Arrivals GMC	121.800
Departures GMC	121.950	Tower [1]	124.225
Tower [2]	129.275	Tower [3]	134.225
'Radio Gatwick'	1584kHz	(Medium Waveband)	

LONDON HEATHROW

Approach & Radar	119.200	Approach & Radar	119.500
Approach & Radar	120.400	Approach & Radar	127.550
Holding Information	113.750	Holding Information	115.100

Departure ATIS	133.075	Arrivals ATIS	127.125
Departures GMC	121.700	Arrivals GMC	121.900
Tower [1]	118.700	Tower [2]	124.750
Tower [3]	118.500	Tower [4]	121.000
Tower [5]	133.075	-------------------------------	---------
'Radio Heathrow'	1584kHz	(Medium Waveband)	

LONDON STANSTED

Approach & Radar	125.550	Departures	121.175
ATIS	127.175	Radar	123.800
Tower	118.150		

LONDONDERRY

Approach & Tower	122.850

LUTON

Approach & Radar	127.300	Approach & Radar	128.750
Approach	129.550	ATIS	120.575
GMC	121.750	Tower	119.975

LYDD

Approach	120.700	Radar	131.300
Tower	120.700		

MANCHESTER

Approach & Radar	121.350	Approach & Radar	119.400
ATIS	128.175	Clearance Delivery	121.700
GMC	121.800	Tower	118.625

MANCHESTER ATC SUB-CENTRE

Radar	124.200	Radar	125.100
Radar	126.650	Radar	133.400
Radar (Pennine RIS)	132.900	Radar	133.050

MIDLAND RADAR

Radar	132.250	Radar	134.300

NEWCASTLE

Approach & Radar	126.350	ATIS	114.250
Radar	118.500	Radar	119.700
Tower	130.600		

NORWICH

Approach & Radar	119.350	Radar	124.250
Tower	118.900		

OXFORD

Approach	130.300	ATIS	118.875
Radar	134.300	GMC	121.750
Tower	118.875		

PERTH

Approach	122.300	Tower	119.800

PRESTON

Approach	122.550	Tower	130.800

PRESTWICK

Approach & Radar	119.450	ATIS	127.125
Approach & Radar	120.550	GMC	121.800
Tower	118.150		

SAMLESBURY

Approach	124.450	Approach	130.800
Tower	130.350		

SCATSCA

Approach & Radar	122.400	Tower	123.600

SHANNON

Approach	120.200	ATIS	130.950
Approach & Radar	121.400	GMC	121.800
Tower	118.700	Zone Radar	121.700
Zone Radar	124.700	Zone Radar	127.500
Zone Radar	131.150	Zone Radar	132.150
Zone Radar	135.600		

SHOREHAM

Approach	123.150	Tower	125.400

SOUTHAMPTON

Approach & Radar	128.850	Radar	120.225
Radar	131.000	Tower	118.200

SOUTHEND

Approach & Radar	128.950	Radar	125.050
Tower	127.725		

STORNOWAY

Approach/Radar & Tower	123.500

SUMBURGH

Approach & Radar	123.150	ATIS	125.850
Radar	130.050	Tower	118.250
Zone Radar	119.250	Zone Radar	118.150

SUNDERLAND

Approach	122.200	Tower	122.700

SWANSEA

Approach & Radar	120.750	Tower	119.700

TEES-SIDE

Approach & Radar	118.850	Radar	128.850
Tower	119.800		

UNST

Approach	123.100	GMC	123.450
Tower	130.450		

WEST MALLING			
AFIS	130.425	Tower	129.850
Displays	130.500		

YEOVIL			
Approach & Radar	130.800	Tower	125.400

RADIODATABASE 2. AIRWAYS AND ATCC CONTROL FREQUENCIES

Low-level Airways

A1	From North 54, 30′ latitude (Turnberry)	Scottish 126.250
		& 128.500
	North 54, to Abeam Stafford above FL155	London 131.050
	Below FL155	Manchester 126.650
	Abeam Stafford to Birmingham above FL135	London 133.700
	Below FL135	Manchester 124.200
	Birmingham to abeam Woodley	London 133.700
	South of Woodley to FIR boundary	London 127.700
A2	TALLA and North 54, 30′ latitude	Scottish 128.500
	North 54, to abeam Lichfield above FL155	London 131.050
	Below FL155	Manchester 126.650
	Abeam Lichfield to abeam Birmingham above	
	FL135	London 134.750
	Below FL135	Manchester 124.200
	Abeam Birmingham to Brookmans Park	London 134.750
	South of Brookmans Park to FIR boundary	London 127.100
A20	FIR boundary to Biggin	London 127.100
	Biggin to abeam Birmingham	London 134.750
	Abeam Birmingham to Pole Hill VOR above	
	FL155	London 131.050
	Below FL155	Manchester 124.200
A25	Dean Cross to North 54, 30′ latitude	Scottish 126.250
	North 54, to REXAM above FL155	London 128.050
	Below FL155	Manchester 133.050
	REXAM to Cardiff	London 131.200
	Cardiff to North 50, 00′ latitude	London 132.600
	North 50 to Channel Islands Zone boundary	Jersey. 125.200,
A30	Inside limits of London FIR	London 127.100
A34	Inside limits of London FIR	London 127.700
A37	Entire route	London 129.600
A47	Pole Hill to Lichfield above FL155	London 131.050
	Below FL155	Manchester 126.650
	Lichfield to abeam Birmingham. Above FL155	London 133.700
	Below FL155	Manchester 124.200
	Abeam Birmingham to Woodley	London 133.700
	South of Woodley to FIR boundary	London 127.700
B1	West of Wallasey above FL155	London 128.050
	Below FL155	Manchester 133.050
	Wallasey to BARTN above FL155	London 128.050

	Below FL155	Manchester 125.100
	BARTN to Ottringham VOR above FL155	London 131.050
	Below FL155	Manchester 126.650
	East of Otttringham VOR (North Sea)	London 134.250
B2	North of TMA	Scottish 124.500
	South of TMA	Scottish 124.900
B3	BEL VOR (Belfast) to Isle Of Man (IOM)	Scottish 124.900
	IOM to Wallasey above FL155	London 128.050
	Below FL155	Manchester 133.050
	Wallasey to Stafford above FL155	London 128.050
	Below FL155	Manchester 125.100
	Stafford to abeam Birmingham above FL155	London 133.700
	Below FL155	Manchester 125.100
	Abeam Birmingham to Brookmans Park	London 133.700
	South of Brookmans Park to FIR boundary	London 127.100
B4	Detling to Brookmans Park	London 127.100
	Brookmans Park to abeam Birmingham	London 134.750
	Abeam Birmingham to ROBIN above FL155	London 134.750
	Below FL155	Manchester 124.200
	ROBIN to Pole Hill VOR above FL155	London 131.050
	Below FL155	Manchester 124.200
	Pole Hill to North 54, 30′ latitude above FL155	London 131.050
	Below FL155	Manchester 126.650
	North 54 to GRICE	Scottish 128.500
B5	Entire route	London 134.250 – 127.950–133.525
B39	MALBY to RADNO	London 131.200
	RADNO to TOLKA	London 128.050
B53	Entire route, above FL155	London 128.050
	Below FL155	Manchester 125.100
G1	West of BRECON	London 131.200
	BRECON to abeam Woodley	London 132.800
	East of Woodley to FIR boundary	London 134.900
R1	ORTAC to Ockham	London 134.450
	Ockham to FIR boundary	London 129.600
R3	Wallasey to ROBIN above FL155	London 128.050
	Below FL155	Manchester 125.100
R8	Southampton to Midhurst	London 134.450
	Midhurst to Dover	London 134.900
R12	Entire route	London 129.600

R14	Inside limits of London FIR	London 131.200

R25	Inside limits of London FIR	London 127.700

R41	ORTAC to Southampton	London 134.450
	Southampton to abeam Compton	London 132.800
	Abeam Compton to Westcott	London 133.700

R84	Entire route	London 134.450

R123	Entire route	London 129.600

R803	Entire route	London 127.700

W923	Entire route above FL155	London 131.050
	Below FL155	Manchester 126.650

W934	Inside limits of London FIR	London 127.700

High-level Airways

UA1	North of North 54, 30' latitude	Scottish 135.850
	North 54 to abeam Lichfield	London 131.050
	Abeam Lichfield to abeam Woodley	London 133.700
	South of Woodley to Upper FIR (UIR) boundary	London 127.700

UA2	Machrihanish to North 54, 30' latitude	Scottish 135.850
	North 54 to TRENT	London 131.050
	TRENT to Brookmans Park	London 133.700
	South of Brookmans Park to UIR boundary	London 127.100

UA20	Entire route	London 127.100

UA25	North of North 54, 30' latitude	Scottish 135.850
	North 54 to South of Wallasey	London 128.050
	South of Wallasey to South of Brecon	London 133.600
	South of Brecon to UIR boundary	London 132.600

UA29	BAKER to LUNDY	London 133.600
	LUNDY to SALCO	London 132.600

UA30	Entire route	London 127.100

UA34	Wallasey to TELBA	London 128.050
	TELBA to abeam Woodley	London 133.700
	Abeam Woodley to UIR boundary	London 127.700

UA37	DANDI to Gabbard	London 134.250
	Gabbard to Detling	London 129.600

UA47	Daventry to Woodley	London 133.700
	South of Woodley to UIR boundary	London 127.700

UA251	Pole Hill to TELBA	London 131.050
	TELBA to EXMOR	London 133.600
UB1	West of Wallasey	London 128.050
	Wallasey to Ottringham VOR	London 131.050
	East of Ottringham (North Sea)	London 134.250
UB2	DALKY to FINDO	Scottish 135.850
	FINDO to KLONN	Scottish 124.050
UB3	Belfast to Isle Of Man	Scottish 135.850
	Isle Of Man to North 53, 00′ latitude	London 128.050
	North 53 to Brookmans Park	London 133.700
	Brookmans Park to Dover	London 127.100
UB4	FINDO to North 54, 30′ latitude	Scottish 135.850
	North 54 to ROBIN	London 131.050
	ROBIN to Brookmans Park	London 134.750
	South of Brookmans Park to UIR boundary	London 127.100
UB5	North of FAMBO	Scottish 135.850
	South of FAMBO	London 132.250
UB10	Inside limits of London UIR	London 133.600
UB11	Inside limits of London UIR	London 134.450
UB29	Abeam Woodley to abeam Brookmans Park	London 133.600
	East of abeam Brookmans Park to UIR boundary	London 129.600
UB39	Midhurst to RADNO	London 133.600
	RADNO to TOLKA	London 128.050
UB40	Entire route	London 133.600
UG1	West of abeam Woodley to UIR boundary	London 133.600
	East of abeam Woodley to UIR boundary	London 134.900
UG4	Inside limits of London UIR	London 132.600
UG11	Inside limits of Scottish UIR	Scottish 124.050
UG106	Inside limits of London UIR	London 134.900
UL1	West of abeam Woodley to UIR boundary	London 133.600
	East of abeam Woodley to UIR boundary	London 134.900
UL7	North of SKATE	Scottish 124.050
	South of SKATE	London 134.250
UL74	Entire route	London 134.250

UL722	Entire route	London 132.600
UR1	West of abeam Lambourne	London 134.450
UR123	East of Lambourne to UIR boundary	London 129.600
UR3	Entire route	London 128.050
UR4	West of Pole Hill VOR	London 128.050
	Pole Hill to Ottringham VOR	London 131.050
	East of Ottringham (North Sea)	London 134.250
UR8	Land's End to Southampton	London 132.600
	Southampton to Midhurst	London 134.450
UR14	Inside limits of London UIR	London 132.600
UR23	West of SAB	Scottish 135.850
	East of SAB	Scottish 124.050
UR24	ORIST to ASPEN	London 134.450
UR25	Entire route	London 127.700
UR37	West of Southampton	London 132.600
	Southampton to abeam Midhurst	London 134.450
	East of abeam Midhurst	London 134.900
UR38	South of FINDO	Scottish 135.850
	North of FINDO	Scottish 124.050
UR41	ORTAC to Southampton	London 134.450
	Southampton to abeam Woodley	London 132.800
	Abeam Woodley to Westcott	London 132.800
UR72	Inside limits of London UIR	London 132.600
UR84	Entire route	London 132.300
UR168	Land's End to CAVAL	London 132.600

RADIODATABASE 3. VHF AIRBAND IN ALPHA-USER ORDER

The change from 50kHz channel spacing to 25kHz occurred only recently. Most of the frequency changes were made early on, but some are still taking place. Every effort has been made, using various NOTAMS and the PILOT, to ensure that the frequencies listed here are accurate. But remember that change is constant.

The term *Radar* refers to the working frequency of the air traffic control officer known as 'Radar', and *not* to the frequency of the actual radar emission itself.

108–136 MHz. VHF Airband In Alpha-User Order

(A.D.F.) DISTRESS	121.500	Abbeyshrule A/G	122.600
Aberdeen ATIS	121.850	Aberdeen Approach & Radar	120.400
Aberdeen FIS	121.250	Aberdeen GMC	121.700
Aberdeen Radar	128.300	Aberdeen Tower	118.100
Aberdeen Tower	121.700	Aberporth Information	122.150
Abingdon Radar MATZ	120.900	Abingdon Tower	130.250
Aer Lingus C/f	131.625	Aer Lingus C/f	131.750
Air Britannia C/f	131.675	Air India C/f	131.600
Airtour Shop – Elstree	129.750	Alconbury LARS & MATZ	134.050
Aldernay & Guernsey Approach	128.650	Alderney Tower	123.600
Alicante Approach	118.800	Alicante GMC	121.700
Alicante Tower	118.150	Amsterdam Approach	121.200
Amsterdam GMC	121.700	Amsterdam Tower	118.100
Andrewsfield A/G	130.550	Andrewsfield Approach	125.550
Anglia Radar	125.275	Anglia Radar	128.925
Audley End A/G	122.350	BA Speedbird C/f	131.975
BA Speedbird C/f	131.800	BA Speedbird C/f	131.850
BA Speedbird C/f	131.900	Badminton A/G	130.425
Ballyfree A/G	122.900	Banff A/G	123.500
Bantry A/G	122.400	Barcelona Approach	119.100
Barcelona GMC	121.700	Barcelona Tower	118.100
Barrow A/G	123.200	Bedford Approach	130.700
Bedford LARS	124.400	Bedford Radar	118.375
Bedford Tower	130.000	Belfast Approach	130.850
Belfast Approach & Radar	120.000	Belfast GMC	121.750
Belfast Radar	120.900	Belfast Radar	122.450
Belfast Tower & Radar	118.300	Belfast Tower (Harbour)	130.750
Bembridge A/G	123.250	Benbecula Tower & Approach	119.200
Benson Radar MATZ	120.900	Bentwaters Radar MATZ	119.000
Biggin Hill AFIS	118.425	Biggin Hill Approach	129.400
Biggin Hill Tower	134.800	Biggin Hill ATIS	115.250
Binbrook LARS	125.350	Binbrook Tower	125.350
Birmingham ATIS	120.725	Birmingham Approach & Radar	131.325
Birmingham GMC	121.800	Birmingham Radar	118.050
Birmingham Tower	118.300	Birr A/G	122.900
Bitteswell Approach	122.500	Bitteswell Approach	130.150
Bitteswell Tower	123.250	Blackbushe A/G	122.300

Blackpool Approach	135.950	Blackpool Radar	119.950
Blackpool Tower	118.400	Bodmin A/G	122.700
Bognor A/G	120.000	Border Radar	128.425
Border Radar	133.875	Borders MMARS	134.300
Boscombe Down Approach	126.700	Boscombe Down Appr' & Radar	125.350
Boscombe Down Radar	130.750	Boscombe Down Tower	130.000
Bourn A/G	129.800	Bournemouth ATIS	121.950
Bournemouth Approach & Radar	118.650	Bournemouth GMC	121.700
Bournemouth Radar	119.625	Bournemouth Tower	125.600
Brawdy Tower & Approach	124.400	Brawby LARS	124.400
Brent Oilfield	122.250	Bridlington A/G	123.250
Bristol (Luls) Tower	120.550	Bristol Approach	127.750
Bristol Approach	127.975	Bristol Approach & Radar	130.850
Bristol Approach & Radar	132.350	Bristol Radar	124.350
Bristol Radar	127.600	Bristol Tower	133.850
Brize Norton Approach	133.750	Brize Norton MMARS	134.300
Brize Norton Tower	126.500	Brize Norton Tower & Approach	119.000
Brooklands A/G	122.350	Brough Approach	118.225
Brough Approach	130.850	Brough Tower	130.550
Brussels Approach	127.150	Brussels GMC	121.875
Brussels Tower	118.600	Burnaston A/G	118.350
Caenarfon A/G	122.250	Cambridge Approach	123.600
Cambridge Radar	130.750	Cambridge Tower	122.200
Cardiff ATIS	119.475	Cardiff Approach & Radar	125.850
Cardiff Radar	120.050	Cardiff Tower	125.000
Carlisle Tower & Approach	123.600	Castlebridge A/G	123.000
Castlebury A/G	122.600	Chester Approach	123.350
Chester Radar	129.850	Chester Tower	124.950
Chivenor LARS & MATZ	130.200	Church Fenton Approach	126.500
Church Fenton Approach	129.150	Church Fenton Tower	122.100
Clackton A/G	122.325	Coltishall Approach & LARS	125.900
Common Aircrew (Air)	123.450	Common RAF Tower/Displays	122.100
Compton Abbas A/G	122.700	Coningsby Approach MATZ	120.800
Connington A/G	123.000	Connington Approach & Radar	134.050
Copenhagen Approach	120.250	Copenhagen GMC	121.900
Copenhagen Tower	118.100	Cork Approach	119.900
Cork GMC	121.800	Cork Radar	118.800
Cork Tower	119.300	Cork Tower	121.700
Cormorant Oil Rigs	129.900	Cottesmore Approach	125.900
Cottesmore LARS	130.200	Cottesmore Tower Appr' & Radar	130.200
Coventry GMC	124.800	Coventry GMC	124.850
Coventry Radar	122.000	Coventry Tower & Approach	119.250
Cowick Hall A/G	130.650	Cranfield Approach & Radar	122.850
Cranfield Tower	123.200	Cranwell Approach MATZ	119.000
Culdrose LARS	134.050	Culdrose Tower	122.100
Cuxwold A/G	122.325	Dan Air C/f	130.650
Denham A/G	130.725	Dishforth Approach	129.500
Dishforth Radar & MATZ	127.750	Doncaster A/G	122.900
Dounreay Tower & Approach	122.400	Dublin Approach & Radar	121.100
Dublin ATIS	118.250	Dublin GMC	121.800
Dublin Radar	128.000	Dublin Tower	119.550
Dublin Tower	122.400	Dublin Tower & Radar	118.600

Dublin VOLMET	127.000	Dundalk A/G	122.900
Dundee Tower & Approach	122.900	Dunkeswell A/G	123.475
Dunsfold Approach & Radar	122.550	Dunsfold Radar	118.825
Dunsfold Tower	124.325	Duxford A/G	123.450
Duxford A/G	123.500	East Colne A/G	122.425
East Midlands Tower	124.000	East Midlands Approach	119.650
East Midlands GMC	121.900	East Midlands Radar	120.125
Eastern MMARS	134.300	Eastern Radar	128.425
Edinburgh ATIS	132.075	Edinburgh Approach & Radar	121.200
Edinburgh Approach & Radar	128.975	Edinburgh GMC	121.750
Edinburgh Radar	124.250	Edinburgh Tower	118.700
Edinburgh Tower	121.700	Eggesford A/G	123.500
Ekofisk Oilfield	122.950	Elstree A/G	122.400
Enniskillen A/G	123.200	Exeter Approach & Radar	128.150
Exeter Radar	119.050	Exeter Tower	119.800
Fairford Approach & Radar	133.750	Fairford Approach MATZ	119.000
Fairford Tower	119.150	Fairoaks A/G	123.425
Farnborough Tower & Approach	125.250	Farnborough LARS	125.250
Farnborough PAR Radar	130.050	Farnborough Tower	122.500
Farranfore A/G	122.600	Felthorpe A/G	123.500
Finningley LARS & MATZ	120.350	Flotta A/G	122.150
Ford A/G	120.000	Fort William Heliport	129.700
Frankfurt Approach	120.800	Frankfurt GMC	121.900
Frankfurt Tower	119.900	Galway A/G	122.500
Gamston (Nottingham) A/G	130.475	Gatwick ATIS	128.475
Gatwick Approach & Radar	119.600	Gatwick Arrivals GMC	121.800
Gatwick Departures ATIS	121.750	Gatwick Departures GMC	121.950
Gatwick Delivery	121.950	Gatwick Radar	118.600
Gatwick Radar	125.875	Gatwick Tower	124.225
Gatwick Tower	134.225	Gatwick Tower	129.275
Geneva Approach	130.150	--	----------
Geneva GMC	121.900	Geneva Tower	118.700
Glagow GMC	121.700	Glasgow Approach & Radar	119.100
Glasgow Radar	119.300	Glasgow Radar	121.300
Glasgow Tower	118.800	Glenrothes A/G	130.450
Goodwood Approach	122.450	Goodwood Tower	119.70
Goodwood Tower	120.650	Greenham Common Approach	130.500
Greenham Common Radar	118.000	Guernsey Radar	118.900
Guernsey Radar	124.500	Guernsey Tower	119.950
Halfpenny Green A/G	123.000	Guernsey GMC	121.800
Halfpenny Green GMC	121.950	Hamble Approach	125.000
Hamble Tower	120.650	Hang-Gliders And Balloons	129.900
Hardwick A/G	129.900	Hatfield Approach & Radar	123.350
Hatfield Operations	123.650	Hatfield Radar	119.300
Hatfield Tower	130.800	Haverfordwest A/G	122.200
Hawarden Radio D/F	123.350	Hawarden Tower	124.950
Hayes Tower A/G	126.650	Heather Oilfield	122.800
Heathrow VFR & helis'	119.900	Heathrow ATIS	121.850
Heathrow Approach	119.200	Heathrow Approach & Radar	119.500
Heathrow Approach & Radar	127.550	Heathrow Arrivals ATIS	127.175
Heathrow Arrivals GMC	121.900	Heathrow Departures ATIS	133.075
Heathrow Departures GMC	121.700	Heathrow Exec Handling A/G	123.650

Heathrow Radar	120.400	Heathrow Tower	118.500
Heathrow Tower	118.700	Heathrow Tower	121.000
Heathrow Tower	124.750	Heathrow Tower	133.075
Hebrides Upp' Con' Area	135.850	Helicopter FIR	129.950
Henstridge A/G	130.250	Hethel A/G	122.350
Highland Radar	126.100	Highland Radar	134.100
Honington Approach & Radar	129.050	Hucknall (Nottingham) A/G	130.800
Huddersfield A/G	122.200	Humberside Approach	121.150
Humberside Approach	123.150	Humberside Tower	118.550
Iberia C/f	131.950	Innishmore A/G	123.000
Inverness Tower & Approach	122.600	Ipswich Tower	118.325
Ipswich Tower	123.250	Islay (Port Ellen) Info'	119.700
Islay A/G	123.150	Jersey Approach & Radar	118.550
Jersey Approach & Radar	120.300	Jersey GMC	121.900
Jersey Tower	119.450	Jersey Zone Radar	120.450
Jersey control	125.200	KLM C/f	131.500
KLM C/f	129.700	KLM C/f	131.650
Kilbrittain A/G	122.900	Kilkenney A/G	122.900
Kilkenney A/G	130.400	Kinloss LARS	119.350
Kirkwall Tower	118.300	Land's End A/G	122.300
Land's End Tower	130.700	Lashenden A/G	122.000
Leavesden Radar	121.400	Leavesden Tower & Approach	122.150
Leconfield Approach	123.100	Lee-On-Solent Tower	135.700
Leeds/Bradford Approach	123.750	Leeds/Bradford Radar	121.050
Leeds/Bradford Tower	120.300	Leeming Approach & Radar	127.750
Leeming LARS	132.400	Leicester Tower	122.250
Lerwick A/G	122.600	Leuchars Approach & LARS	126.500
Linton Approach & Radar	129.150	Linton LARS	129.150
Linton LARS	129.550	Little Snoring A/G	122.400
Liverpool Approach & Radar	119.850	Liverpool Radar	118.450
Liverpool Tower	118.100	Loganaire C/f	130.650
London (City) Approach	132.700	London (City) Radar	128.025
London (City) Tower	121.775	London (City) Tower	119.425
London ATCC	123.900	London ATCC	125.800
London ATCC	125.950	London ATCC	126.300
London ATCC	126.450	London ATCC	128.400
London ATCC	128.900	London ATCC	132.050
London Control	127.100	London Control	119.200
London FIR	124.775	London Hand-Over to Euro ATC	132.200
London Heliport Tower	122.900	London FIR	134.700
London FIR S/W	124.600	London FIR S/W	124.750
London MMARS	134.700	London Military Radar	124.750
London VOLMET	135.375	London VOLMET north	126.600
London VOLMET south	128.600	London control	132.600
London control	131.050	London control	133.700
London control	134.250	London control	134.750
London control	135.050	London control	127.100
London control	132.450	London control	131.200
London control	135.250	London control	133.450
London control	134.250	London control	134.450
London control	132.800	London control	127.100
London control	133.525	London control	133.600

Londonderry Tower & Approach	122.850	Lossiemouth Approach & Radar	119.350
Lossiemouth Tower	118.900	Luton ATIS	120.575
Luton ATIS	133.975	Luton Approach	128.750
Luton Approach	129.550	Luton Approach & Radar	127.300
Luton GMC	121.750	Luton Tower	119.975
Luton Tower	120.575	Lydd Tower & Approach	120.700
Lydd Tower & Radar	131.300	Lyneham Tower Appr' & Radar	123.400
Machrihanish Approach & MATZ	119.700	Madrid Approach	119.900
Madrid GMC	121.700	Madrid Tower	118.500
Malaga Approach	118.450	Malaga GMC	121.700
Malaga Tower	118.150	Manchester (Barton) A/G	122.700
Manchester ATIS	128.175	Manchester Approach	121.350
Manchester Approach & Radar	119.400	Manchester Clearance Deliv'	121.700
Manchester GMC	121.800	Manchester Tower	118.625
Manchester Tower	128.625	Manchester control	124.200
Manchester control	125.100	Manchester control	126.650
Manchester control	133.050	Manston Approach	129.450
Manston Approach & LARS	126.350	Manston Radar	123.000
Manston Radar	123.300	Manston Tower	128.775
Manston Tower	124.900	Marham Approach & Radar	124.150
Marham LARS	124.150	Medway Marine	122.250
Midland Radar	132.250	Mildenhall Approach	124.050
Mildenhall Approach	129.050	Mildenhall Tower	122.550
MMARS	132.250	Mona Aero Club frequency	122.000
National Gliders	130.100	National Gliders	130.125
National Gliders	130.400	Netherthorpe A/G	123.500
Newcastle ATIS	114.250	Newcastle Approach & Radar	118.500
Newcastle LARS	126.350	Newcastle Radar	126.950
Newcastle Tower	119.700	Newtonards A/G	123.500
North Denes A/G	120.450	North Scottish Helicopters	123.050
Northampton A/G	122.700	Northolt Radar	125.800
Northolt Radar	125.950	Northolt Radar	128.900
Northolt Radar	129.125	Northolt Radar	130.350
Northolt Tower & Approach	134.150	Norwich Approach & Radar	119.350
Norwich Radar	124.250	Norwich Tower	118.900
Nottingham A/G	122.800	Oceanic Clearance (Shanwick)	133.800
Old Sarum A/G	123.575	Old Warden A/G	123.050
Orion Ops C/f	131.775	Ostend Approach	120.600
Ostend GMC	121.900	Ostend Tower	118.700
Oxford Approach	130.300	Oxford Departures & ATIS	121.950
Oxford GMC	121.750	Oxford Tower	118.875
Pailton Testing Centre	126.050	Palma Approach	119.150
Palma GMC	121.700	Palma Tower	118.300
Pan Am C/f	131.400	Paris (Bourget) Approach	121.150
Paris (Bourget) GMC	121.900	Paris (Bourget) Tower	119.100
Paris (Orly) Approach	120.850	Paris (Orly) GMC	121.700
Paris (Orly) Tower	118.700	Paris (de Gaulle) Approach	121.150
Paris (de Gaulle) GMC	121.600	Paris (de Gaulle) Tower	119.250
Pennine Radar	132.900	Penshanger A/G	120.250
Penzance Heliport	118.100	Perth Approach	122.300
Perth Tower	119.800	Plymouth Approach	123.200
Plymouth Tower	122.600	Plymouth Tower	133.550

Popham A/G	129.800	Portland Approach & Radar	124.150
Powerscourt A/G	123.450	Predannock Radar & MATZ	134.050
Prestwick ATIS	127.125	Prestwick Approach & Radar	120.550
Prestwick GMC	121.800	Prestwick Radar	119.450
Prestwick Radar	121.800	Prestwick Tower	118.150
RAF Leuchars GMC	120.800	RAF bases Approach & Radar	123.300
Redhill A/G	123.225	Rochester Tower & Radar	122.250
Rome Approach	119.200	Rome GMC	121.900
Rome Tower	118.700	Ronaldsway (I.O.M.) Radar	118.200
Ronaldsway Approach & Radar	120.850	Ronaldsway Radar	125.300
Ronaldsway Tower	118.900	Rush Green A/G	122.350
Sabena Ops C/f	131.950	Samlesbury Approach	122.550
Samlesbury Tower	130.350	Samlesbury Tower	130.800
Sandown A/G	123.500	Sandown A/G	123.500
Sandtoft A/G	130.425	Scampton MATZ	127.350
Scatsca Radar	122.400	Scatsca Tower & Approach	123.600
Scilly Isles Tower	123.150	Scottish & Highland MMARS	134.300
Scottish FIR	123.150	Scottish control	126.250
Scottish control	124.900	Scottish control	124.500
Scottish control	133.200	Scottish control	135.850
S.A.R. (scene of search)	123.100	Seething A/G	122.600
Shannon ATIS	130.950	Shannon Approach	120.200
Shannon Approach & Radar	121.400	Shannon Centre	121.700
Shannon GMC	121.800	Shannon Tower	118.700
Shannon Tower	121.800	Shannon Zone	124.700
Shannon Zone Control	135.600	Shannon Zone control	127.500
Shannon Zone control	132.150	Shannon control	131.150
Shanwick Oceanic Clearance – Aircraft reg' E (UK) of 30 deg West			127.650
Shanwick Oceanic Clearance – Aircraft reg: W (US) of 30 degs West			123.950
Shanwick Aeradio	127.900	Shawbury Approach & Radar	124.150
Shawbury LARS	124.150	Sherburn-In-Elmet Tower Appr'	126.500
Sherburn-In-Elmet A/G	122.600	Shetland Radar	118.150
Shobden A/G	123.500	Shoreham Approach	123.150
Shoreham Tower	125.400	Sibson Tower	122.300
Silverstone A/G	121.075	Skegness A/G	130.450
Skulthorpe Radar	124.500	Sleap A/G	122.450
Sleap A/G	124.150	Southampton Approach	128.850
Southampton Approach	120.225	Southampton Radar	131.000
Southampton Tower	118.200	Southend ATIS	121.800
Southend Approach	128.950	Southend Radar	125.050
Southend Radar	129.450	Southend Tower	127.725
Southport Heliport	122.950	Sproatley A/G	129.900
St. Mawgan Approach & LARS	126.500	St. Mawgan Radar	125.550
St. Mawgan Tower	123.400	Stansted ATIS	127.175
Stansted Approach & Radar	126.950	Stansted Radar	123.800
Stansted Radar	125.550	Stansted Tower	118.150
Stapleford A/G	122.800	Staverton Radar	122.900
Staverton Tower & Approach	125.650	Stornaway Tower & Approach	123.500
Strubby Heliport C/f	122.375	Strubby Gliders	130.400
Sturgate A/G	130.300	Sumburgh ATIS	125.850
Sumburgh Approach	123.150	Sumburgh Approach & FIS	119.250
Sumburgh Radar	123.150	Sumburgh Radar	130.050

Sumburgh Tower	118.250	Sunderland Approach	122.200
Sunderland Tower	122.700	Sutton Bank Gliders	130.400
Swansea Radar	120.750	Swansea Tower/Approach/Radar	119.700
Swanton Moreley A/G	123.500	TWA C/f	131.600
Tatenhill A/G	122.200	Tees-Side Approach & Radar	118.850
Tees-Side Approach & Radar	128.850	Tees-Side Tower	119.800
Thruxton A/G	130.450	Tibenham A/G	130.100
Tibenham A/G	130.400	Tingwall A/G	122.600
Tiree A/G	122.700	Tollerton A/G	122.800
Topcliffe Approach	122.100	Topcliffe Approach	127.750
Topcliffe Approach	132.400	Topcliffe Tower	125.000
Unst Tower & Approach	130.350	Upper Heyford Appr' & MATZ	128.550
Valley & Mona Appr' & Radar	132.350	Valley LARS	134.350
Valley Radar & MATZ	134.250	Various C/f	129.700
Various C/f	129.750	Various C/f	130.600
Various C/f	131.450	Various C/f	131.550
Various oil rigs	123.550	Viking Approach – helis	129.950
Waddington LARS & MATZ	127.350	Walney Tower	123.200
Wardair C/f	129.700	Warton Tower	130.800
Wattisham LARS	135.200	Wellsbourne A/G	130.450
Welshpool A/G	124.150	West Freugh Radar & MATZ	130.050
West Freugh Tower	122.550	West Malling A/G	129.850
West Malling Tower	130.875	Weston Super Mare Approach	129.250
Weston Super Mare Tower	122.500	White Waltham A/G	122.600
Wick Tower & Approach	119.700	Wickenby A/G	122.450
Winfield A/G	123.500	Wittering Radar & MATZ	130.200
Woodbridge MATZ	119.000	Woodford Approach	130.050
Woodford Radar	130.750	Woodford Tower	126.925
Woodvale A/G	123.500	Woodvale Tower/Approach/Radar	121.000
Common Fire & Rescue GMC	121.600	Wycombe Air Park A/G	126.550
Wyton Radar & MATZ	134.050	Yeovil Approach & Radar	130.800
Yeovil Tower	125.400	Yeovilton Approach & Radar	127.350
Yeovilton LARS	127.350	Zurich Approach	120.750
Zurich GMC	121.900	Zurich Tower	119.700

RADIODATABASE 4. VHF AIRBAND IN ALPHA-USER ORDER

Short Wave Airband – In Alpha-User Order

All Frequencies in KiloHertz; All Modes USB Unless Stated Otherwise

Abadan Radio	6624	Aeroflot Moscow C/f	13220
Aeroflot Moscow	13241	Aeronautical Channel	2851
Aeronautical Channel	3019	Africa ATC	13336
Africa/Indian Ocean ATC	17961	Africa ATC	5493
Air France C/f	6526	Air France C/f	10093
SAR: Nimrods. Nighttime	3022	SAR: Air-Sea-Rescue	3085
Akrotiri Air	4730	Algiers Radio	6575
Alia Royal Jordan Airlines	13225	Aljouf	3095
Amman Air	3453	Amman Air C/f	3523
Amsterdam Aeradio	21925	Anchorage/Tokyo Airports	13282
Andrews Air Force Base	4645	Andrews Air Force Base	4720
Andrews Air Force Base	6680	Andrews Air Force Base	6730
Andrews Air Force Base	6738	Andrews Air Force Base	6756
Andrews Air Force Base	6760	Andrews Air Force Base	13215
Andrews Air Force Base	18027	Antarctica Bases	14415
Asia ATC	6571	Athens Air C/f	3013
Atlantic Coast Aeradio	17985	Australia In-Flight Comms	13205
Australian Air Force	18003	BA Speedbird C/f	6658
Baghdad	5603	Beirut	3404
Baghdad. Beirut VOLMET	3001	Berlin Aeradio	3478
Berlin Aeradio	6598	Berlin-Malta R/T Link	5661
Berne Aeradio	21980	Berne Aeradio	2959
Berne Aeradio	10069	Beunos Aires VOLMET	5477
Beunos Aires VOMET	11319	Bodo Aeradio	6544
Bodo Aeradio	4666	BA Speedbird C/f	5535
BA Speedbird C/f	8977	BA Speedbird C/f	10072
BA Speedbird C/f. [UK]	17922	BA Air-To-Ground	3481
BA C/f [Out of Heathrow]	13356	BA C/f [Out Of Heathrow]	6568
BA C/f [Concorde]	10093	BA C/f [Concorde]	17965
BA C/f [Concorde]	21886	Cairo MET: (MODE=RTTY)	5559
Canada Military VOLMET (P)	15035	Canaries Aeradio	5598
Canaries & Ghardia ATC	2854	Casablanca. Canaries Aeradio	6610
Caribbean ATC	2887	Caribbean ATC	5520
Casablanca. Canaries ATC	3432	Central America ATC	3455
Central/East Pacific ATC	2869	Central/West Pacific ATC	2998
Central/South American ATC	13297	COSMOS Satellites Downlink	19452
Royal Navy, Culdrose	6825	Cyprus Flight-Watch	15046
Cyprus Flight-Watch	18018	Dharan & Gizan	2095
Distress Calling Frequency	3022	East Caribbean R/T Network	5484
East Caribbean R/T Network	11367	Edinburgh Rescue SAR	5695
Europe ATC	10084	Europe R/T Network	2910
Europe R/T Network	6582	Europe R/T Network	6586
Europe R/T Network	4689	Europe VOLMET	5574
Europe/South America Link	3479	Far East ATC	3470
Far East ATC	10066	Far East ATC	13309
Far East VOLMET	6675	Far East/Australia ATC	13318

Far East/South American ATC	17907	French Air Force (MODE=CW)	4465
G4MDQ CW Calling Frequency	7010	Gander Aeradio	6547
Gander Airport (P)	4675	Gander Aeradio	3485
Gander/New York VOLMET	6604	Gander/New York VOLMET	8868
Gander/New York VOLMET	10051	Gander/New York VOLMET (P)	13270
Gibraltor Flight-Watch	4742	Goeteborg	5724
Great Yarmouth SAR	5484	Great Yarmouth SAR	3488
Great Yarmouth Helis. SAR	5645	Havanna Aeradio (MODE=CW)	17936
Iberia C/f	3060	Iberia C/f	5529
Iberia C/f	6589	Iberia C/f	6592
Indian ATC	3476	Indian Ocean ATC	5634
Interflug C/f	4738	Interflug C/f	6753
Interflug C/f	4745	International Air-Sea-Rescue	5589
International SAR Coordination	5670	Jeddah Air Operations	15022
Kaliningrad	10054	Kenya Airlines C/f	6640
Kiev Aeradio	2893	Kiev Aeradio	6553
KLM C/f	5645	KLM C/f	5532
LAARS	11233	Lanzarote. Stavanger	3023
Las Palmas & Frankfurt	21967	Las Palmas & Hong Kong	17940
Leningrad	3116	Leningrad	4728
London/Falkland Islands R/T Link. Call=GLY31. Mode=LSB			11420
Lufthansa C/f	4687	Lufthansa C/f	5645
Lufthansa C/f	6637	Lufthansa C/f	10078
Mediterranean LORAN net	15723	Miami SIGNET	10050
Middle East ATC	5667	Middle East ATC	13312
Cairo. Benghazi ATC	3467	Damascus. Kuwait ATC	2992
Middle East/Africa Traffic	13288	Middle East/USSR Traffic	5638
Minsk Aeradio	2902	Mobile ATC 6637-6670 @3kHz	6637
Montivideo VOLMET	13294	Moscow Aeradio	13247
Moscow MET	2941	Moscow MET	4663
NASA Cape Canaveral	9006	NASA Cape Canaveral	9043
NASA Cape Canaveral	19640	NASA Cape Canav' Call=AFE7	7461
NATO AWACS – MAGIC Com'd	15691	NATO AWACS – MAGIC Com'd	6762
NATO Turkey	4875	New York Aeradio VOLMET	13271
New York VOLMET	3485	New York VOLMET	5652
New Zealand/Antartica R/T	8997	Nigeria Aeradio	23210
North Africa VOLMET	6574	N./Africa/S.Pacific R/T Link	13279
North Atlantic R/T	3419	North Atlantic R/T	11303
North Atlantic R/T	13288	North Atlantic R/T	13328
North Atlantic R/T	13352	North Atlantic R/T	17941
North Atlantic R/T	17965	North Atlantic R/T (P)	4675
North Atlantic R/T (P)	5598	North Atlantic R/T (P)	5616
North Atlantic R/T (P)	5649	North Atlantic R/T (P)	8825
North Atlantic R/T (P)	8864	North Atlantic R/T (P)	8879
North Atlantic R/T (P)	8891	North Atlantic/Indian Ocean	13291
North Atlantic/Indian Ocean	13306	North East Asia ATC	5658
North Pacific ATC	2932	North Pacific ATC	5628
North Pacific ATC	10048	North Pacific ATC	13294
North West Africa ATC	5652	North West Africa ATC	6535
North West Pacific LORAN	15875	Oakland USA VOLMET	2980
Oakland USA VOLMET	5519	Oakland USA VOLMET	8903
Oakland USA VOLMET	13344	Pacific ATC	6532

Pacific ATC	13251	Pacific ATC	13300
Pacific ATC	17904	Pailton Radio Testing Centre	3467
Paris Aeradio. Bahrain	21943	Peru VOLMET	13415
Plymouth SAR (Daytime)	5680	Prestwick Airport	6705
Qantas C/f	6526	Qantas C/f	10093
RAAF/RNZAF R/T Link	8975	RAF	6702
RAF	6726	RAF	9032
RAF (P)	11234	RAF In-Flight	15031
RAF Akrotiri	6751	RAF Alconbury (USAF)	6741
RAF Bampton	13257	RAF Edinburgh	6757
RAF Finningley	6697	RAF Finningley	6751
RAF Gibraltar	15737	RAF Lond' (MODE=USB & CW)	4500
RAF Lossiemouth	4540	RAF Mildenhall (USAF)	6741
RAF Pitreavie	6697	RAF – ARCHITECT	4744
RAF – ARCHITECT	11204	RAF Scotland	5471
RAF Strike Command	5729	RAF Strike Command	6738
RAF Strike Command	18018	RAF United Kingdom	4870
RAF Uphaven	4742	RAF VOLMET (24 hours)	4722
RAF West Drayton	6690	RCAF	13254
RCAF Canada/Europe R/T Link	18012	Reykjavik OCA	2962
Reykjavik OCA. Beirut	2899	Royal New Zealand Air Force	15053
Rome Naval Base	6700	Rostov	6617
Rosyth Royal Navy Base (CW)	6717	Fleet Air Arm (Royal Navy)	5456
Royal Navy – Gibraltar	6762	Salyut Satellites Beacon	19989
Salyut Satellites Beacon	20008	Salyut Satellites Downlink	19946
Salyut-7 Satellites	19955	Saudi Aeradio	21994
Saudi Airways C/f	5545	SAR – Nighttime Coordination	3023
SAR Supplementary	3939	Shannon VOLMET	3413
Shannon VOLMET	5640	Shannon VOLMET	13264
Shannon VOLMET (P)	5505	Shannon VOLMET (P)	8957
Shanwick Oceanic	5625	Shanwick Oceanic	8854
Shanwick Oceanic	17936		
Shanwick Oceanic Central & Northern Tracks East of 30 West (UK)			2962
Shanwick Oceanic Central & Northern Tracks East of 30 West (UK)			5649
Shanwick Oceanic Central & Northern Tracks East of 30 West (UK)			8879
Shanwick Oceanic Central & Northern Tracks East of 30 West (UK)			13306
Shanwick Oceanic Central & Northern Tracks West of 30 West (US)			8864
Shanwick Oceanic Central & Northern Tracks West of 30 West (US)			2899
Shanwick Oceanic Central & Northern Tracks West of 30 West (US)			5616
Shanwick Oceanic Northern Tracks, Uncontrolled Airspace			2971
Shanwick Oceanic Northern Tracks, Uncontrolled Airspace			4675
Shanwick Oceanic Northern Tracks, Uncontrolled Airspace			8891
Shanwick Oceanic Southern Tracks – All Aircraft			3016
Shanwick Oceanic Southern Tracks – All Aircraft			5598
Shanwick Oceanic Southern Tracks – All Aircraft			8825
Singapore Airlines C/f	5526	South Africa ATC	2878
South America ATC	5526	South America ATC	10024
South American R/T Link	8882	South American R/T Link	11343
South Asia ATC	6556	South Atlantic OCA	5565
South Atlantic OCA	6535	South Atlantic OCA	13315
South Pacific OCA	5643	COSMOS Satellites – Recovery	20005
Salyut/COSMOS Downlink	19954	Soviet Satellites, Beacons	19996

Soyuz Spacecraft Beacons	20008	Soyuz Telemetry Downlink	19955
St. Johns VOLMET	6753	Stockholm Aeradio	15685
Stockholm Aeradio	11222	Stockholm Aeradio Phone-Patch	5541
Tripoli & Algiers Aeradios	3419	Tunis Aeradio	3411
RAF Bases UK/Abroad R/T	11185	US Coastguard (Aircraft)	15081
US Coastguard (Aircraft)	15084	US Hurricane Warning R/T net	8993
US MARS Stations	14383	US MARS Stations	14390
US Navy	15051	US Navy	18009
US Navy – Antartica	13974	US Navy World R/T Network	6880
US Navy MARS Stations	14441	US Navy World CW Network	11186
US Navy – Air-To-Ship	8984	USA 'SKYKING'	6764
USAF Air-To-Ground	6640	USAF	4744
USAF	6712	USAF	11176
USAF	11243	USAF	15041
USAF	18019	USAF – Anderson Base, Guam	14560
USAF Within US Working.	11182	USAF Air Traffic	6683
USAF Air Traffic	6684	USAF Alconbury	4477
USAF Athens	6820	USAF Azores Base	7735
USAF Azores Base	15066	USAF Croughton	6750
USAF Cyprus Flight-Watch	6751	USAF Iceland	6760
USAF In-Flight Comms.	4732	USAF In-Flight Comms.	11118
USAF In-Flight Comms.	13201	USAF Japan	15038
USAF MARS Stations	14606	USAF 'VIP'	6715
USSR ATC	6592	West Caribbean R/T Network	6561
West Caribbean R/T Network	8840	West Drayton VOLMET	11200
World Hi-Jack Alerting	17925	Yeovilton Royal Navy Base	6708

RADIODATABASE 5. UHF AIRBAND IN ALPHA-USER ORDER

UHF Airband – Mostly Military. All Frequenzies in mHz

Abingdon Approach	299.100	Abingdon Tower	256.500
Air Refuelling	298.950	Alconbury Approach	306.850
Alconbury Tower	283.600	Barkston Heath Approach	367.200
Barkstone Heath Tower	307.700	Bedford Approach	265.100
Bedford Tower	241.350	Benson Approach	299.100
Benson Tower	398.700	Bentwaters Approach	292.700
Bentwaters Tower	257.800	Binbrook Tower	242.650
Boscombe Down Approach	313.200	Boscombe Down Tower	242.200
Brawby Approach	387.350	Brawby Tower	378.600
Bristol Filton Approach	244.700	Bristol Filton Tower	290.350
Brize Norton ATIS	363.500	Brize Norton Approach	246.450
Brize Norton GMC	288.850	Brize Norton Ops	382.550
Brize Norton Tower	294.750	Brough Approach	234.450
Brough Tower	310.350	Chivenor Approach	309.900
Chivenor Tower	318.150	Church Fenton Approach	381.800
Church Fenton GMC	307.400	Church Fenton Tower	359.800
Coltishall Approach	379.200	Coltishall GMC	269.450
Coltishall Tower	288.850	Coningsby Approach	370.900
Coningsby Tower	234.950	Cosford Approach	234.100
Cosford Tower	292.100	Cottesmore Approach	266.050
Cottesmore GMC	307.400	Cottesmore Tower	246.400
Cranfield Approach	372.100	Cranfield Tower	341.800
Cranwell Approach	297.900	Cranwell GMC	276.000
Cranwell Tower	380.100	Culdrose ATIS	305.600
Culdrose Approach	292.700	Culdrose GMC	310.200
Culdrose Tower	289.100	Dishforth Approach	341.500
Dishforth Tower	309.300	Dunsfold Approach	241.800
Dunsfold Tower	287.500	Eastern Radar [1]	343.850
Eastern Radar [2]	288.500	Eastern Radar [3]	247.400
FIS (Eastern Region)	340.050	Fairford Approach	246.450
Fairford GMC	276.550	Fairford Tower	380.000
Finningly Approach	298.500	Finningly GMC	276.000
Finningly Tower	315.700	Greenham Common Approach	313.200
Greenham Common Tower	266.800	Highland Radar	285.750
Honington Approach	355.350	Honington GMC	318.150
Honington Tower	233.850	Kemble Approach	363.100
Kemble Tower	335.550	Kinloss Approach	319.000
Kinloss Ops	394.700	Kinloss Tower	287.000
Lakenheath Approach	361.600	Lakenheath GMC	248.450
Lakenheath Tower	231.500	Leeming Approach	387.800
Leeming GMC	394.500	Leeming Ops	281.000
Leeming Tower	382.100	Leuchars Approach	257.700
Leuchars GMC	290.700	Leuchars Ops	308.700
Leuchars PAR	318.100	Leuchars Tower	269.000
Linton-On-Ouse Approach	357.500	Linton-On-Ouse Tower	246.800
Lossiemouth Approach	319.000	Lossiemouth GMC	314.100
Lossiemouth Tower	291.000	Lyneham ATIS	367.600
Lyneham Approach	315.750	Lyneham GMC	318.950

Lyneham Tower	293.100	Machrihanish Approach	287.050
Machrihanish Tower	285.600	Manston Approach	352.500
Manston Tower	362.100	Marham Approach	265.800
Marham Ops	241.450	Marham Tower	275.350
Middle Wallop Approach	314.900	Middle Wallop Tower	267.100
Midland Radar [1]	227.600	Midland Radar [2]	264.550
Midland Radar [3]	307.500	Mildenhall ATIS	259.400
Mildenhall Approach	355.350	Mildenhall GMC	297.400
Mildenhall Tower	250.000	Netheravon Approach	254.000
Netheravon Tower	233.400	Northolt ATIS	268.900
Northolt Approach	377.500	Northolt Ops	253.650
Northolt Tower	275.650	Odiham ATIS	269.700
Odiham Approach	341.000	Odiham Tower	378.550
Plymouth Rescue NATO SAR	282.800	Plym'th Rescue Scene-Of-Search	244.600
Portland Approach	317.800	Portland Tower	291.000
RAF Tain Helicopters	248.700	Red Arrows Air-To-Air	243.450
Samlesbury Approach	286.750	Samlesbury Tower	254.350
Scampton Approach	362.500	Scampton GMC	307.400
Scampton Tower	265.900	Sculthorpe Approach	246.700
Sculthorpe GMC	277.600	Sculthorpe Tower	378.050
Shawbury Approach	364.100	Shawbury GMC	382.200
Shawbury Tower	359.200	Shetland Radar	285.650
St. Athan Approach	230.300	St. Athan Tower	352.900
St. Mawgan Approach	352.850	St. Mawgan Ops	245.600
St. Mawgan Tower	286.200	Swinderby Approach	307.100
Swinderby Tower	313.300	Topcliffe Approach	382.600
Topcliffe Tower	293.100	Uphaven Approach	259.850
Uphaven Tower	357.000	Upper Heyford ATIS	263.950
Upper Heyford Approach	316.850	Upper Heyford GMC	309.700
Upper Heyford Ops	293.200	Upper Heyford Tower [1]	313.650
Upper Heyford Tower [2]	257.800	Valley Approach	378.900
Valley GMC	387.500	Valley Tower	307.400
Waddington Approach	255.500	Waddington GMC	352.750
Waddington Tower	383.600	Warton Approach	286.750
Warton Tower	254.350	Wattisham Approach	299.200
Wattisham Tower	353.500	West Freugh Approach	387.550
West Freugh Tower	241.350	Wethersfield Approach	362.300
Wethersfield GMC	308.100	Wethersfield Tower	293.600
Wittering Approach	362.300	Wittering GMC	340.050
Wittering Tower [1]	251.050	Wittering Tower [2]	257.800
Woodbridge Approach	292.700	Woodbridge GMC	307.400
Woodbridge Ops	315.200	Woodbridge Tower	257.800
Woodford Approach [1]	241.900	Woodford Approach [2]	240.950
Woodford Tower [1]	240.950	Woodford Tower [2]	241.900
Yeovilton Approach	276.700	Yeovilton GMC	265.700
Yeovilton Tower	381.000		

RADIODATABASE 6. AIRBANDS FREQUENCY RANGES HF/VHF/UHF

Short Wave Airbands Range (Civil & Military)

2194–2300kHz	General Aeronautical Band	Channel Spacing=3kHz
2300–2495kHz	General Aeronautical Band	Channel Spacing=3kHz
2505–2850kHz	General Aeronautical Band	Channel Spacing=3kHz
2850–3025kHz	Civil Aeronautical Band	Channel Spacing=3kHz
3025–3155kHz	Military Aeronautical Band	Channel Spacing=3kHz
3400–3500kHz	Civil Aeronautical Band	Channel Spacing=3kHz
4438–4650kHz	General Aeronautical Band	Channel Spacing=3kHz
4650–4700kHz	Civil Aeronautical Band	Channel Spacing=3kHz
4700–4750kHz	Military Aeronautical Band	Channel Spacing=3kHz
5480–5680kHz	Civil Aeronautical Band	Channel Spacing=3kHz
5680–5730kHz	Military Aeronautical Band	Channel Spacing=3kHz
6525–6685kHz	Civil Aeronautical Band	Channel Spacing=3kHz
6685–6765kHz	Military Aeronautical Band	Channel Spacing=3kHz
8815–8965kHz	Civil Aeronautical Band	Channel Spacing=3kHz
8965–9040kHz	Military Aeronautical Band	Channel Spacing=3kHz
10000–10100kHz	Civil Aeronautical Band	Channel Spacing=3kHz
11175–11275kHz	Military Aeronautical Band	Channel Spacing=3kHz
11275–11400kHz	Civil Aeronautical Band	Channel Spacing=3kHz
13260–13360kHz	Civil Aeronautical Band	Channel Spacing=3kHz
15000–15100kHz	Military Aeronautical Band	Channel Spacing=3kHz
17970–18030kHz	Military Aeronautical Band	Channel Spacing=3kHz
21870–21925kHz	Fixed Aeronautical Band	Channel Spacing=3kHz
108.000–117.975mHz	Radio Navigation	Channel Spacing=50kHz
118.000–137.000mHz	VHF R/T Airband	Channel Spacing=25kHz
137.000–138.000mHz	Satellite Space–Earth downlinks	
149.900–150.050mHz	Satellite Radionavigation	
225.000–368.600mHz	Military UHF Airband	Channel Spacing=25kHz
328.600–335.400mHz	ILS Glide Slope	
335.400–340.000mHz	Military UHF Airband	Channel Spacing=25kHz
455.000–461.000mHz	Airport Ground Movement Controller	
960.000–1215.000mHz	DME–Radionavigation	

RADIODATABASE 7. OCEANIC HF FAMILY GROUP FREQUENCIES

Frequency Group	OCA	QRG	QRG	QRG	QRG	QRG	QRG
GROUP A	Gander	3016	5598	8825	13306	17946	
	New York	3016	5598	8825	13306		
	San Juan	3016	5598	8825	13306		
	Santa Maria	3016	5598	8825	13306		
	Shanwick	3016	5598	8825	13306		
	Paramaribo	3016	8825				
	Canaries	5598	8825				
GROUP B	Gander	2899	5616	8864	13291	17946	
	Reykjavic	2829	5616	8864	13291		
	Shanwick	2829	5616	8864	13291		
GROUP C	Gander	2872	5649	8879	11336	13306	17946
	Reykjavic	2872	5649	8879	13306		
	Shanwick	2872	5649	8879	11336	13306	
GROUP D	Bodo	2971	4675	8891	11279	13291	17946
	Cambridge Bay	2971	4675	8891	11279		
	Churchill	2971	4675	8891			
	Gander	2971	4675	8891	13291		
	Iqaluit	2971	4675	8891	11279		
	Reykjavic	2971	4675	8891	11279	13291	17496
	Shanwick	2971	4675	8891	13291		
	Sondrestrom	2971	4675	8891	11279		

And what the *Groups* relate to.

GROUP A
Transatlantic Southern routes – ALL aircraft.

GROUP B
Transatlantic Central & Northern routes; aircraft registered WEST of 30 degrees WEST (US & Canadian aircraft).

GROUP C
Transatlantic Central & Northern routes; aircraft registered EAST of 30 Degrees WEST (UK and European aircraft).

GROUP D
Transatlantic Northern routes; aircraft outside the Organised Track System.

RADIODATABASE 8. VHF/HF COMPANY AND SPECIAL INTEREST FREQUENCIES

VHF Company Frequencies

Aer Lingus	131.625	Aer Lingus	131.750
Air Europe	131.775	Aviaco	131.575
Air France	131.425	Air France	131.550
Air UK	129.750	Air UK	131.450
American Airlines (Gatwick)	130.650	Birmingham Executive	131.850
British Midland Airways	129.750	British Midland Airways	131.475
British Midland Airways	131.575	Britannia	131.675
British Airways	131.800	British Airways	131.850
British Airways	131.900	Dan Air	130.650
Dan Air	131.550	Dan Air	131.650
Euroair	130.600	KLM	130.600
KLM	131.550	KLM	131.600
Monarch Airlines	130.650	Monarch Airlines	131.525
Qantas	131.850	Servisair*	130.600
Servisair	131.600	Speedbird London Ops	130.600
Trans World Airways	130.650	Trans World Airways	131.600
Virgin Atlantic	130.650	Worldways	130.650

* Same frequency for ALL Servisair Agency Airports.

Shortwave Airband Radio Frequencies Of Special Interest

PORTISHEAD RADIO
(Third-party HF phone patches)
3482, 5610, 8170, 8185, 8960, 11306, 12133, 17405, 18210, 19510, 20065kHz.
USB

(Third-party HF phone patches)

BERNE AERADIO
4654, 6643, 10069, 13205, 18023kHz. USB

STOCKHOLM RADIO
5541, 8930, 11345, 13342, 17916, 23210kHz. USB

BRITISH AIRWAYS
(Company HF R/T Network)
5535, 8921, 10072, 13333, 17922kHz. USB

AIR FRANCE
6526, 6637, 10093kHz. USB

QANTAS
6526, 10093, 13342kHz. USB

SEARCH AND RESCUE
3023, 3488, 3939, 5420, 5670, 5680, 5695, 6760, 8893, 9025, 18271kHz. USB

INTERNATIONAL SEARCH & RESCUE
8364kHz. USB.

LATCC & SCATCC AIRWAYS FREQUENCIES
London Sectors: 134.450/134.425
Bristol Sector: 132.800
Scottish Sector: 128.500
Daventry Sector: 134.750

VHF/HF Airband Radio Frequencies: Speedbird–Concorde

Frequencies on which to maintain a listening watch are:
OUTBOUND: Heathrow Departures. LATCC. 132.800/133.600mHz.
At 28,000 feet. London Control: 132.600/132.950mHz.

OCEANIC. BA 'companies': 3481, 5535, [6568], 8921, 8977, 10072, [10093],
13333, [13356], 17922, [17965], [21886] kHz.

(Note – frequencies within brackets have special significance to Concorde
flights. Listen around 0700–0800 GMT)

INBOUND: At 50 North/12 West. LATCC: 132.600 – Heathrow Approach
information.
At 37,000 feet over South Wales: 132.800/133.600mHz.
HEATHROW: Heathrow Approach.

SPACE–WATCH: Satellite Band Listening

US Military Satellites
MODE=NBFM

243.850–243.900	Leasat – US Navy Department.
243.960–244.100	Fleetsatcom – US Navy Department.
248.800–249.400	Marisat.
249.350–249.850	Leasat – US Air Force
260.775–268.350	Fleetsatcom – US Navy Department.

EXAMPLE
Channel X–Ray, Fleetsatcom West. 261.675mHz. Phone patches. Mode=
Narrowband FM

NASA SPACE SHUTTLE

(Shuttle Space–To–Earth R/T Link.)
(Also EVA (Space–walk) Talk–back to flight deck.)
259.700, 270.000, 296.800mHz. Mode=NBFM

Miscellaneous VHF Frequencies Of Interest

Shanwick Oceanic Clearances:
123.950mHz – USA etc. 127.650mHz – Europe etc.

Shanwick Atlantic Organised Tracks:
133.800mHz.

Flight Information Services (FIS):
131.050/134.250/132.600mHz.

Scottish Information:
124.900mHz.

London Information North of Bravo 1:
134.700mHz.

London Information South of Bravo 1:
124.600/124.750mHz.

RADIODATABASE 9. UK AIRFIELD A/G FREQUENCIES

Aberporth AFIS	122.150	Andrewsfield A/G	130.550
Audley End	122.350	Badminton	130.425
Banf	123.500	Barra	130.650
Barrow	123.200	Barton	122.700
Bembridge (IOW)	123.250	Biggin Hill	129.400
Blackbushe	122.300	Bodmin	122.700
Boulmer	123.100	Bourne	129.800
Bridlington	123.250	Caernarvon	122.250
Clackton	122.325	Compton Abbas	122.700
Connel Gliders	130.400	Conwick Hall	130.650
Denham	130.725	Derby (Burnaston)	118.350
Doncaster	122.900	Duxford	123.500
Earls Colne	122.425	Eggesford	123.500
Elstree	122.400	Fairoaks	123.425
Farranfore	122.600	Feldon (Helicopters)	129.750
Felthorpe	123.500	Fenland	123.050
Fife	130.450	Flotta	122.150
Fort William (Helicopters)	129.700	Foulsham	130.650
Galway	122.500	Gamston	130.475
Grimsby	122.350	Halfpenny Green AFIS	123.000
Halton	130.425	Hardwick	129.900
Haverfordwest	122.200	Hethel	122.350
Hitchin	122.350	Hucknal	130.800
Huddersfield	122.200	Hull	129.900
Islay AFIS	123.150	Isle Of Skye	130.650
Isle Of Wight	123.500	Land's End	130.700
Lashendon	122.000	Lee On Solent	135.700
Leicester	122.250	Lerwick	122.250
Little Snoring	122.400	Mona AFIS	122.000
Netherthorpe	123.500	Newtonwards	123.500
North Weald	130.500	Northampton	122.700
Nottingham (Tollerton)	122.800	Nottingham (Lowdham)	123.050
Nuthampstead	123.050	Old Sarum	123.575
Old Warden	123.050	Penshanger	120.250
Penzance	118.100	Pocklington	130.100
Popham	129.800	Portland	122.100
Redhill	123.225	Rochester AFIS	122.250
Salisbury	130.150	Sandown (IOW)	123.500
Sandtoft	130.425	Scilly Isles	123.150
Seething	122.600	Sherburn-In-Elmet	122.600
Shipham	123.050	Shobden	123.500
Silverstone	121.075	Skegness	130.450
Sleap	122.450	South Marston	130.425
Stapleford	122.800	Stourport	122.950
Sutton Bank Gliders	130.400	Tatenhill	122.200
Thruxton	130.450	Tibenham	130.100
Tiree AFIS	122.700	Wellesbourne	130.450
Welleyfoot Park	123.500	York Gliders	130.400

Part 6
Appendices

APPENDIX 1. VOLMET SERVICES, INFORMATION AND SCHEDULES

Aviators like to know what the weather's like at their destination airports, and what conditions are expected to be en-route. The VOLMET and airport ATIS services provide this information on a continuous broadcast basis, which also takes a lot of the pressure off airband radio telephony frequencies as well.

Pilots flying VFR can get the same information from whichever Flight Information Service they're using at the time. The VHF VOLMET services are designed to cover the country, often making use of relay stations, to boost signal levels in areas of known poor reception. For those aircraft flying out of range of the VHF VOLMETS, such as across the North Atlantic Ocean, there are the various world-wide HF VOLMETS, which can be picked up many miles away.

VHF VOLMET Stations (24 Hours)

LONDON VOLMET NORTH. 126.600mHz. Covering:
London Heathrow, Manchester International, Glasgow, Edinburgh, Prestwick, Belfast, Aberdeen, Newcastle and Leeds/Bradford. Main transmitter located at Great Dunn Fell, Cumbria.

LONDON VOLMET SOUTH. 128.600mHz. Covering:
London Heathrow, London Gatwick, Luton, Bournemouth, Stansted, East Midlands International, Southend, Cardiff and Jersey. Transmitters located at Isle Of Wight and Warlingham (South of London); Frequency Off-Set: +/−5kHz (128.595–128.605mHz).

LONDON VOLMET MAIN. 135.375mHz. Covering:
London Heathrow, London Gatwick, Birmingham International, Manchester International, Prestwick, Dublin, Schipol (Amsterdam), Brussels and Charles De Gaulle (Paris).Transmitters located at Isle Of Wight and Warlingham (South of London); Frequency Off-Set: +/−5kHz (135.370-135.380mHz)

DUBLIN VOLMET. 127.000mHz. Coverage:
Dublin, Shannon, Cork, Belfast, Glasgow, Prestwick, Manchester International, London Heathrow and London Gatwick.

SCOTTISH VOLMET. 125.725mHz. Coverage:
Aberdeen, Aldergrove (Belfast), Edinburgh, Glasgow, Inverness, London Heathrow, Prestwick, Stornoway and Sumburgh.

HF VOLMET Stations Worldwide

([P]=Primary Operating Frequency)

SHANNON VOLMET. 3413, 5640, 5505[P], 8957, 13264kHz.

Schedule and report areas/airports

Hour +00 mins	Brussels, Hamburg, Frankfurt, Cologne, Bonn, Dusseldorf and Munich Airports
Hour +05 mins	Shannon, Prestwick, London Heathrow, Amsterdam, Manchester International and London Gatwick

Hour +10 mins	Copenhagen, Stockholm, Goteborg, Bergen, Oslo, Helsinki, Dublin and Barcelona
Hour +15 mins	Madrid, Lisbon, Paris Orly, Santa Maria, Paris Charles De Gaulle and Lyon
Hour +20 mins	Rome, Milan, Zurich, Geneva, Turin and Athens
Hour +30 mins	Farnkfurt, Cologne, Brussels, Hamburg, Dusseldorf and Munich
Hour +35 mins	Amsterdam, Manchester International, London Gatwick, Shannon, Prestwick and London Heathrow
Hour +40 mins	Copenhagen, Stockholm, Goetborg, Bergen, Oslo and Helsinki
Hour +45 mins	Santa Maria, Athens, Paris Charles De Gaulle, Madrid, Lisbon, Paris Orly and Lyon
Hour +50 mins	Zurich, Geneva, Rome, Milan, Turin and Athens.

GANDER VOLMET. 3485, 6604, 8868, 10051 13270[P]kHz.

Schedule and report areas/airports

Hour +20 mins	Montreal Dorval, Montreal Mirabel, Toronto, Ottawa, Gander, Goose and Halifax
Hour +25 mins	Winnipeg, Edmonton, Calgary, Sydney, Frobisher and Sondrestrom
Hour +50 mins	Gander, Goose, Halifax, Montreal Dorval, Montreal Mirabel, Toronto and Ottawa
Hour +55 mins	Sydney, Frobisher, Sondrestrom, Winnipeg, Edmonton and Calgary.

NEW YORK VOLMET. 3485, 5652, 6604, 10051 13270

Schedule and report areas/airports

Hour +00 mins	Detroit, Chicago, Cleveland, Niagara Falls, Milwaukee and Indianapolis
Hour +05 mins	Bangor, Pittsburgh, Windsor Locks, St. Louis, Syracuse and Minneapolis
Hour +10 mins	New York, Newark, Boston, Baltimore, Philadelphia and Washington
Hour +15 mins	Bermuda, Miami, Nassau, Freeport, Tampa and West Palm Beach
Hour +30 mins	Niagara Falls, Milwaukee, Indianapolis, Detroit, Chicago and Cleveland
Hour +35 mins	Windsor Locks, St. Louis, Bangor, Pittsburgh, Syracuse and Minneapolis
Hour +40 mins	Baltimore, Philadelphia, Washington, New York, Newark and Boston
Hour +45 mins	Nassau, Freeport, Bermuda, Miami, Tampa, Palm Beach.

ST. JOHN'S MILITARY VOLMET. 6753, 15035kHz.
(Note only available 1200-2300z)

Schedule and report areas/airports

Hour +40 mins	Montreal, Halifax, Shearwater, Greenwood, Sumerside, Sydney, Yarmouth, Stephenville, St. John's, Gander,

New Brunswick, Chatham, Moncton, Goose Bay, Sable Island, St, Anthony, Bermuda, Keflavik

ROYAL AIR FORCE VOLMET. 4722[P], 6737, 11200kHz.

Schedule and report areas/airports

Continuous	Aldergrove (Belfast), Benson, Binbrook, Brize Norton, Coningsby, Finningly, Honington, Kinloss, Leeming
Broadcast	Leuchars, Heathrow, Gatwick, Lossiemouth, Lyneham, Manchester International, Manston, Marham, Northolt, Odiham, Prestwick, St. Mawgan, Valley, Waddington, Wattisham, Wyton and Yeovilton

Understanding VOLMET Transmissions

VOLMET metereological broadcasts are made up from computer-stored, spoken words and phrases which are spliced together and then transmitted. They provide weather information concerning a target airport or area. The format of the broadcast is:

1 VOLMET station name
2 Name of target airport/area
3 Time of observation(s)
4 Surface wind details
5 Horizontal visibility range
6 Runway visual range
7 General weather details
8 Cloud information
9 Current ambient temperature
10 The 'Dew Point'
11 The 'QNH'
12 Weather trends

Examples

'This is London VOLMET MAIN (1). Manchester International (2) at one-four-zero-zero. (3). One-two-zero-zero degrees at twelve knots. (4). two-zero-zero metres (5), Runway Visual Range one-zero-zero metres (6), recent showers. (7). Five Okta, at two towsand feet. (8). Temperature fifteen (9) – Dew Point twelve. (10). QNH one-zero-one-eight. (11). Nosig (12).'

'This is London VOLMET MAIN. Prestwick at zero-four-zero-zero. two-eight-zero at one-fife knots. Cavok. Temperature eleven, dew point zero-eight. QNH one-zero-one-eight. Nosig.'

Okta	The extent to which the sky is covered by clouds is divided into eight parts, each one being called an Okta. 'Eight Okta' indicates total overcast. Below 5,000 feet it is usual to state the height at which the obscuring cloud lies. e.g. 'Three Oktas, tree-towsand feet.' Which means that at 3,000 feet, three-eighths of the sky is obscured by cloud. Apart from cumulo-nimbus (CB) formations,

cloud above 5,000 feet is assumed to be of academic interest only to aviators.

Dew Point   The temperature, in degrees Celsius, at which water vapour in the atmosphere will condense to form fog. When the ambient temperature (also Celsius) and the Dew Point are the same, then there is fog.

Weather Change Indicators

Gradu   At the end of the VOLMET transmission there is usually a word which signifies what the weather is expected to do next, the *Trend*. Gradu indicates that any changes are expected to occur at a constant rate – or gradually.

Rapid   The changes are expected to occur quickly – in less than thirty minutes.

Tempo   The change is expected to last for less than sixty minutes.

Inter   Changes are expected constantly, fluctuating from minute to minute, indicating very unsettled weather.

Tend   A change is expected to occur slowly, throughout the current VOLMET period.

CAVOK   When visibility is greater than 10 kilometres, and there's no cloud below 5,000 metres, no rain or snow, and no fog or mist around either, then both ceiling and visibility are perfect for flying, and the acronym CAVOK – pronounced 'KAV – OKAY' is used in a VOLMET broadcast to indicate this situation. It replaces parts 5, 6, 7 and 8 of my example VOLMET transmission, listed previously.

Nosig   Signifies that the weather is not expected to change at all during the current period. No Significant . . .

SIGMET   Used before a VOLMET broadcast to indicate that a Significant Metereological change has (or more usefully, *is* about to) occur. It is usually followed by a single word warning of the expected problem, such as: Sigmet – snow, Sigmet – thunder.

Military VOLMET Information

METAR

The RAF have a much simpler system of broadcasting the availability and cloud cover at their airbases; they use a code system of colours. They do use the usual VOLMET format as well, although the military refer to weather information as METAR. Listen on 4722kHz.

Surface Visibility	Colour	Cloud Basc
8 Km	Blue	2,500 feet
5 Km	White	1,500 feet
3.7 Km	Green	700 feet
1.8 Km	Yellow	300 feet
0.9 Km	Amber	200 feet
less than 0.9 Km	Red	Below 200 feet
0 Km	Black	Airfield Unusable.

Usually, the name of the airfield is given and then the colour. For example: 'Coningsby – White. Finningly – Green. Benson – Amber.'

APPENDIX 2. INTERNATIONAL AIRCRAFT REGISTRATION LETTERS

3A	Monaco	3B	Mauritius
3C	Equatorial Guinea	3D	Swaziland
3X	Guinea	4R	Sri Lanka
4U	UN Flights	4W	Yemen
4X	Israel	5A	Libya
5B	Cyprus	5H	Tanzania
5N	Nigeria	5R	Madagascar
5T	Mauritania	5U	Niger
5V	Togo	5W	Western Samoa
5X	Uganda	5Y	Kenya
6O	Somalia	6V	Senegal
6Y	Jamaica	7P	Lesotho
7Q	Malawi	7T	Algeria
8P	Barbados	8Q	Maldives
8R	Guyana	9G	Ghana
9H	Malta	9J	Zambia
9K	Kuwait	9L	Sierra Leone
9M	Malaysia	9N	Nepal
9Q	Zaire	9U	Burundi
9V	Singapore	9XR	Rwanda
9Y	Trinidad & Tobago	A2	Botswana
A3	Tonga	A40	Oman
A5	Bhutan	A6	United Arad Emirates
A7	Qatar	A9	Bahrain
AP	Pakistan	B	China/Taiwan
C2	Nauru	C3	Andora
C5	The Gambia	C6	Bahamas
C9	Mozambique	CC	Chile
CCCP	Soviet Union	CF/CG	Canada
CN	Morocco	CP	Bolivia
CS	Portugal	CU	Cuba
CX	Uruguay	D	West Germany
D2	Angola	D4	Cape Verde Islands
D6	Comores Islands	DDR	East Germany
DQ	Fiji	EC	Spain
EI	Ireland	EL	Liberia
EP	Iran	ET	Ethiopia
F	France	G	Great Britain
H4	Solomon Islands	HA	Hungry
HB	Switzerland	HC	Ecuador
HH	Haiti	HI	Dominican Republic
HK	Colombia	HL	South Korea
HP	Panama	HR	Honduras
HS	Thailand	HV	The Vatican
HZ	Saudi Arabia	I	Italy
J2	Djibouti	J3	Grenada
J5	Guinnea Bissau	J6	St. Lucia
J7	Dominica	J8	St. Vincent
JA	Japan	JY	Jordon
LN	Norway	LV	Argentina

LX	Luxembourg	LZ	Bulgaria
MI	Marshall Islands	N	USA
OB	Peru	OD	Lebanon
OE	Austria	OH	Finland
OK	Czechoslovakia	OO	Belgium
OY	Denmark	P	North Korea
P2	Papua New Guinea	P4	Aruba
PH	Netherlands	PJ	Netherlands Antilles
PK	Indonesia	PP/PT	Brazil
PZ	Surinam	RDPL	Laos
RP	Philippines	S2	Bangladesh
S7	Seychelles	SE	Sweden
SP	Poland	ST	Sudan
SU	Egypt	SX	Greece
T2	Tuvalu	T3	Kiribati
T7	San Marino	TC	Turkey
TF	Iceland	TG	Guatemala
TI	Costa Rica	TJ	Cameroon
TL	Central African Republic	TN	Congo
TR	Gabon	TS	Tunisia
TT	Chad	TU	Ivory Coast
TY	Benin	TZ	Mali
V2	Antigua	V3	Belize
V8	Brunei	VH	Australia
VN	Vietnam	VP/F	Falkland Islands
VP/LK	St. Kitts	VP/LL	Nevis
VP/LM	Montserrat	VP/LZ	Virgin Islands
VQ/T	Turks & Caicos Islands	VR/B	Bermuda
VR/C	Cayman Islands	VR/G	Gibraltar
VR/H	Hong Kong	VT	India
X/ABC	Mexico	XT	Burkina Faso
XU	Kampuchea	XY/Z	Burma
YA	Afghanistan	YI	Iraq
YJ	Vanuata	YK	Syria
YN	Nicaragua	YR	Romania
YS	El Salvador	YU	Yugoslavia
YV	Venezuela	Z	Zimbabwe
ZA	Albania	ZK	New Zealand
ZP	Paraguay	ZS	South Africa

APPENDIX 3. BIBLIOGRAPHY

For those who want to know more about the various subjects within the Handbook, I can thoroughly recommend the following list of books. Most may be purchased from any (good) local bookshop. Where I had difficulty, and you probably will too, I've given a direct address. I have added a few succinct comments about each title in the list: only when you've read them will you appreciate their perception! (*Note*: prices correct at time of going to press.)

Flight Routings 1990 by T.T. Williams
ISBN 0 9514431 1 9
Price £4.95
Yearly A to Z guide to airline flights within the UK. Gives company, flight number, aircraft type, time and airport. Very useful.
Available direct from:
T.T. Williams, 'Greenfields', 126 Haven Road, Haverfordwest, Pembrokeshire. SA61 1DP. Or your local bookshop

Flightcheck by T.A.S.
Price £1.00
Lists all Manchester Airport's scheduled and other flights, each issue covering 1 month.
Published monthly, by T.A.S.
Available from Manchester Airport, or direct from T.A.S.

ABC Airport Operations by R.D. Palmer
ISBN 0 7110 1823 5
Price £5.95
Everything you ever wanted to know about airport operations. Worth every penny.
Published by Ian Allan Ltd.

UK Airport Handbook by The Aviation Data Centre
ISBN 0 946141 35 5
Price £4.95
Fairly useful guide, covering the BAA-owned airports only.
Published by Browcom Group PLC

Airborne From Manchester by Alan Grocott
Price £2.99
Useful beginner's guide, based on Manchester Airport
Published by C.M.C. Publishers.

Flying The Big Jets by Stanley Stewart
ISBN 0 906393 69 8
Price £12.95
Brilliant book which explains all the basics, and puts you onto the flight-deck of a transoceanic Boeing 747. Recently reprinted, but could really do with bringing up to date.
Published by Airlife, England.

Appendices

Flying For Fun by Keith Carey
ISBN 0 85059 705 6
Price £8.95
Covers just about every possible way to fly, from light aircraft to (voluntary) jumping out of airplanes armed with nothing more than a silken umbrella! Published by Patrick Stephens Ltd.

ABC Air Traffic Control (3rd Edition) by Graham Duke
ISBN 0 7110 1842 1
Price £3.95
Excellent book concerning all aspects of ATC, and is well up-to-date too. However, the section on airband radio is a little misleading in places. If you only ever buy the one book on ATC, make sure it's this one.

United Kingdom Air Traffic Control by David Graves
ISBN 1 85310 078 1
Price £10.95
This book is sub-titled *A Layman's Guide*. Ha! Mr Graves really does get into detail, and gives all the background material I had to leave out. Fairly up-to-date and easy to read.
Published by Airlife, England.

Civil Airliner Recognition by Peter R March
ISBN 0 7110 1820 0
Price £5.95
Covers most of the major airliners, with identifying features and excellent colour photographs. Useful section at the end to help differentiate between similar types.
Published by Ian Allan Ltd.

Civil Aircraft Markings 1990 by Alan J Wright
ISBN 0 7110 1908 8
Price £4.25
Records details of UK and some overseas aircraft registrations, enabling a spotter to find out from a registration, who owns the aircraft, and its type etc.
Published yearly, by Ian Allan Ltd.

Air Traffic Radio
ISBN 0 947609 02 4
Price £2.99
Guide to VHF/UHF airband radio frequencies, airports, airfields and military. No HF coverage. Brief introduction to ATC.
Published on a regular basis, so is fairly up-to-date, by Scott Willen Publications.
In case of difficulty, this book is available from Lowe Electronics, at Matlock, as well as the specialist aviation hobby shops.

The Lowe Airband Guide by Lowe Electronics Ltd
Price £1.00
Written in-house, this brilliant little book represents the best pound's-worth of information you'll ever come across. It deals with the subject from the

viewpoint of an absolute beginner. Highly recommended indeed! Only available from Lowe Electronics.

Air Band Radio Handbook (3rd Edition) by David J Smith
ISBN 1 85260 339 9
Price £6.99
Mr Smith is an ex-ATC man, consequently he covers the ATC parts well, even though the updated version still needs to be updated! However, be very careful with the airband radio section, especially the little tip about shoving a self-tapping screw into the headphone socket of your receiver. Do this, and you *will* blow your receiver's audio IC to pieces, which is a very, very costly repair!
Published by Patrick Stephens Ltd.

High In The Sky by J. Davies, K. Barker and A. McKenzie
Price £4.25
This book is primarily a SelCal/Aircraft Registration index, but does have a useful introduction concerning (usually high-level) airways radio frequencies, and HF airband.
Published by The Aviation Hobby Shop.

HF Oceanic Airband Communications by Bill Laver
ISBN 0 9512729 9 3
Price £3.50
Excellent introduction into HF Airband radio, and then provides details of HF Aeronautical Radio Frequencies between 2–23mHz.
Published by Spa Publishing Ltd.

VHF/UHF Airband Frequency Guide by Bill Laver
ISBN 0 9512729 8 5
Price £5.95
Short introduction into VHF Airband radio, then lists airband frequencies in the VHF/UHF range. The section dealing with airways frequencies isn't as useful as it only gives the frequencies, not the areas they apply to.
Published by Spa Publishing Ltd.

Addresses for various publishers may be found in Appendix 9 – Useful Addresses.

APPENDIX 4. GLOSSARY OF TERMS

A/G	Air-To-Ground Frequency
ACC	Area Control Centre
ADF	Automatic Direction Finding
ADR	Advisory Route
AFIS	Aerodrome Flight Information Service
AFTN	Aeronautical Fixed Telecommunications Network
AGL	Above Ground Level
AIC	Aeronautical Information Circular
AIP	Aeronautical Information Publication
AIRAC	Aeronautical Information Regulation & Control
AIS	Aeronautical Information Services
AMSL	Above Mean Sea Level
ATA	Actual Time of Arrival
ATC	Air Traffic Control (Generic)
ATCC	Air Traffic Control Centre
ATD	Actual Time of Departure
ATIS	Automatic Terminal Information Service
ATS	Air Traffic Services
ATZ	Aerodrome Traffic Zone
Abeam	Any point 90 degrees left/right of current position
Acknowledge	Confirm reception and understanding
Active	The current runway end in use
Approach	Aerodrome ATC Approach Controller
Avgas	Aviation Gasoline
Backtrack	Return along runway/taxiway
Base leg	Turning towards runway on airport VFR traffic circuit
Box	Pilot's reference to VHF transmitter, Box 1/2/3 etc.
Break	Quick break between ATC R/T messages
C/f	Company Frequency
CAVOK	Ceiling And Visibility OKAY (Excellent)
CB	Cumulo-Nimbus cloud formation
CIP	Commercially Important Person
CTR	ConTRol Zone
CW	Continuous Wave (Morse code)
Cancel	Annul previous request/instructions
Check	Confirm to your own satisfaction the following . . .
Circuit	Airport VFR traffic circuit
Cleared	Proceed under the conditions stated
Climb	Increase vertical height of aircraft
Confirm	Reception of ATC R/T, proposed actions
Contact	Establish R/T contact with the following service . . .
Control	ATC Area Control service
DME	Distance Measuring Equipment
DVOR	Doppler Vhf Omni-Range
Descend	Decrease vertical height of aircraft
Direct	Pilot request to route direct to a location or navaid
EAT	Expected Approach Time
EET	Estimated Elapsed Time
ETA	Estimated Time of Arrival
ETD	Estimated Time of Departure

Established	Aircraft correctly lined-up on the ILS
FIC	Flight Information Centre
FIR	Flight Information Region
FIS	Flight Information Service
Final	Final approach to the runway prior to landing
Flight Level	Vertical height of aircraft above Transition Altitude
GCA	Ground Controlled Approach
GMC	Ground Movement Controller
GPU	(auxilliary) Ground Power Unit
Ground	Aerodrome ATC Ground Movement Controller
H24	24 hours operation
HF	High Frequency (1200kHz–30mHz)
Heading	Current magnetic compass course being steered
Heavy	Pilot-speak, a large aircraft (747, DC10 etc.)
IFR	Instrument Flight Rules
ILS	Instrument Landing System
IMC	Instrument Metereological Conditions
INS	Inertial Navigation System
LARS	Lower Airspace Radar Service
LATCC	London Air Traffic Control Centre
LLRS	Low-Level Radar Service
LOM	Locator Outer Marker
LORAN	LOng RANge Navigation (over-the-horizon radar)
Leaving	Exiting one Flight Level for another (up or down)
Line-up	Aircraft moves onto runway and lines-up, ready for take-off
Localiser	Part of ILS
London	London Air Traffic Control Centre - West Drayton
MARS	Middle Airspace Radar Service and military affiliated radio station.
MATZ	Military Air Traffic Zone
MET	Metereological
MLS	Microwave Landing System
MMARS	Military Middle Airspace Radar Service
MNPS	Minimum Performance Navigation Specifications
Maintain	Hold the present course, altitude, air speed
Manchester	Air Traffic Control Sub-Centre, Manchester Airport
NDB	Non-Directional Beacon
NOTAM	NOTices to AirMen
Negative	No. Permission not granted. Do not proceed
Not Above	ATC height restriction on an aircraft
OAC	Oceanic Area Control
OACC	Oceanic Air Traffic Control Centre
OCA	Oceanic Control Area
Orbit	Aircraft circling, usually in a landing queue
Out	End of R/T Message. (Obsolete)
Out of	Pilot-speak, leaving one Flight Level for another
Outer Marker	Airport approach fan beacon, part of the ILS
Over	End of R/T transmission, I expect a reply
PAR	Precision Approach Radar
PAPIS	Precision Approach Path Indicating System
PPI	Plan Position Indicator (type of radar display)
PPR	Prior Permission Required (found on air charts)

Pass Message	What is your request?
Passing	Pilot-speak, passing through a Flight Level
Pax	Passengers
Pop-Up	Radar image which suddenly appears from nowhere on-screen
Procedure Turn	Aircraft turning to intercept the ILS beams
Pushback	Aircraft being pushed backwards, by a tug, away from the stand
QDM	Obsolete Q-code, magnetic course to steer
QFE	Atmospheric pressure reading at the runway threshold
QNH	Atmospheric pressure above mean sea level
QRE	Frequency
R/T	Radio Telephony
RAS	Radar Advisory Service
RIS	Radar Information Service
RP	Reporting Point – along an airway
RPL	RePetitive flight pLan
RTTY	Radio TeleTYpe – teleprinters etc.
RVR	Runway Visual Range
Radar	ATC Radar service, not the fundamental radar emission
Reaching	Aircraft arriving at a Flight Level
SAR	Search And Rescue
SCATCC	SCottish Air Traffic Control Centre
SELCAL	SELlective CALling; tone-encoded squelch system on HF radio
SID	Standard Instrument Departure
SIGMET	SIGnificant METereological information
SNOWTAM	Warning of aerodrome snow conditions
SRA	Special Rules Area
SRZ	Special Rules Zone
SSR	Secondary Surveillance Radar
SST	Supersonic Transport
STAR	Standard Terminal Arrival Route (opposite of SID)
Scanner	Multi-frequency range radio receiver
Scottish	Scottish Air Traffic Control Centre (Prestwick Airport)
Shanwick	HF Oceanic Radio station near Shannon, Ireland
Slot	Approved Departure Time (pilot-speak)
Squawk	Identifying code set on SSR transponder
Stand	Aircraft parking/loading position at airport
Standby	Wait until called again on R/T
Start-up	Permission for aircraft to start engines
TACAN	TACtical Air Navigation – military navaid
TAF	Terminal Area Forecast – weather
TMA	Terminal control (Manoeuvering) Area
TVOR	Terminal VOR
Take-off	Aircraft cleared to take-off along runway
Taxi	Aircraft manoeuvering towards/from the runway
Tower	Aerodrome ATC Controller
Track	Aircraft's true direction of travel across the ground
UAR	Upper Air Route
UHF	Ultra High Frequency (200–900mHz)
UIR	Upper (Flight) Information Region

USAF	United States Air Force
UTA	Upper Control Area
UTC	Universal Time Coordinated (GMT)
VASIS	Visual Approach Slope Indicating System
VDF	VHF Direction Finding
VFO	Variable Frequency Oscillator – radio tuning control
VFR	Visual Flight Rules
VHF	Very High Frequency (30–200mHz)
VIP	Very Important Person
VMC	Visual Metereological Conditions
VOLMET	Metereological Information for aircraft & aviators
VOR	Vhf Omni-direction Range
VORTAC	VHF Tactical Navigation beacon (VOR and TACAN)
VVIP	Very, Very Important Person. Honest!
Vacating	Aircraft leaving a Flight Level (see Out Of, Leaving etc.)
Visibility	Pilot's horizontal/vertical limit of clear vision
Vortex Wake	Air turbulence caused by vortices from wing tips
WX	Weather
Waypoint	Reporting position, usually a latitude/longitude, or a name

APPENDIX 5. MAGAZINES FOR PLANE SPOTTERS

There is a large number of magazines dealing with the subject of aviation, but very few for the plane spotter. Most of the Aviation Societies (see Appendix 10) put out their own magazines for members, and these can occasionally be purchased by non-members as well. (Prices correct at time of going to press.)

Aviation News
Monthly magazine which, as its title suggests, contains all the latest news from the aviation world. Has a column, written by David J. Smith – author of *The Airband Radio Handbook*, called *RADIO WATCH* which follows the same format as the magazine, providing latest news on the subject of airband radio frequencies etc. and some background detail.
Price £1.65

Shortwave Magazine
Monthly magazine which is aimed primarily at short wave listeners, and contains articles on techniques, frequencies and radio receiver reviews. Also has a regular monthly airband column, written by Godfrey Manning, called AIRBAND. The column acts primarily as a reader's forum relying heavily on reader input for its monthly topics.
Price £1.60
Published by PW Publishing Ltd.

Ham Radio Today, *CB – Citizens' Band* and *Scanners International*
The first two magazines may at first sight appear to contain little of interest for the plane spotter. However, they both contain the third magazine which is also monthly and is given away free!
    Scanners International is a magazine for the scanning radio receiver enthusiast, and contains two regular airband columns, written by myself and Jonathan Clough. My column is called CIVIL AIRBAND, Jonathan's is MILITARY AIRBAND. Each month, my column deals with an aspect of aviation and explains it to the newcomer. There's information from the various aviation societies, and of course, all the latest news on frequencies and airband radio operations.
    Scanners International, as far as I know, is the only magazine which has a monthly military airband column, as well as my own civil airband bit.

APPENDIX 6. SUPPLIERS OF AIRBAND RADIO RECEIVERS AND HOBBY SHOPS

Lowe Electronics
Chesterfield Road
Matlock
Derbyshire
DE4 5LE
Telephone 0629–580800
FAX 0629–580020

For those who can't get to Matlock – which is a shame, because it really is a beautiful spa town, well worth a visit in its own right, and an ideal family day out – they also have branches around the country.

Lowe Electronics branches are:
Glasgow: 041–945–2626
Darlington: 0325–486121
Cambridge: 0223–311230
Barry: 0446–721304
London: 081–429–3256
Bournemouth: 0202–577760

Nevada Communications
189 London Road
North End
Portsmouth
Telephone 0705–662145
FAX 0705–690626

Raycom Communications Systems Ltd
International House
963 Wolverhampton Road
Oldbury
West Midlands
B69 4RJ
Telephone 021–544–6767
FAX 021–544–7124

Dressler Communications Ltd
191 Francis Road
Leyton
London
E10 6NQ
Telephone 081–558–0854
FAX 081–558–1298

Bredhurst Electronics Ltd
High Street
Handcross
West Sussex
RH17 6BW
Telephone 0444–400786

Waters & Stanton
18–20 Main Road
Hockley
Essex
SS5 4QS
Telephone 0702–206835/204965

SRP Trading
Unit 20 Nash Works
Forge Lane
Belbroughton
Stourbridge
Worcestershire
Telephone 0562–730672
FAX 0562–731002

C.M. Howes Communications
Eydon
Daventry
Northants
NN11 6PT
Telephone 0327–60178

Howes DcRx HF airbands receiver and digital display kits.

Remote Receiver Control By Computer

Mr Barry Jenkins
32 Marsh Crescent
High Halstow
Kent
ME3 8TJ

Computer control of the Yaesu FRG-8800/FRG9600 receivers. IBM PC (or compatible) computer. Price £41.50 inc. postage (price correct at time of going to press).

E.M.P. Ltd
51 High Street
Portland
Dorset
DT5 1JQ
Telephone 0305–826900

Computer control of the Icom R7000, Yaesu FRG9600 and AOR AR2002/AR3000 receivers) Price £149.99 inc. postage etc. Works with any computer (price correct at time of going to press).

Lowe Electronics
Computer control of the AOR AR2002/AR3000 series scanners using a dedicated interface & ROM software, works with any computer.

Remote Receiver Control By Vox Switch

P Beckett
3 Pasture Close
Whitmore
Staffordshire
ST5 5DQ

VOX switch for tape recorders, designed for internal receiver fitting (no box), kit price £9.95, ready-built £19.95 inc. postage (prices correct at time of going to press).

Aerotronic Controls Ltd
Halesfield 22
Telford
Shropshire
TF7 4QX
Telephone 0952–586329

VOX switch (built), boxed, with audio leads, price £48.95 (price correct at time of going to press).

Aviation Hobby Shops

Note: most of these shops sell airband receivers and Scanners, antennas, binoculars and telescopes, airways charts etc. Books, magazines and other aviation oriented material.

Javiation
Carlton Works
Carlton Street
Bradford
West Yorkshire
BD7 1DA
Telephone 0274–732146
FAX 0274–722627

The Aviation Society (T.A.S.)
The Aviation Shop
Spectator Terraces
Manchester International Airport
Manchester
M22 5SZ
Telephone 061–499–0303

The Aviation Hobby Centre
First-Floor, Terminal Building
Birmingham International Airport
Birmingham
Telephone 021–782–6560

The Aviation Hobby Shop
Department CAM: 4 Horton Parade
Horton Road
West Drayton
Middlesex
Telephone 0895–442123

Flightdeck
58-62 Lower Hillgate
Stockport
Cheshire
SK1 3AN
Telephone 061–480–8080

Air Supply
83b High Street
Yeadon
Leeds
LS19 7TA
Telephone 0532–509581

APPENDIX 7. SUPPLIERS OF AIRWAYS CHARTS & MAPS

British Airways AERAD Charts

British Airways Aerad Customer Services
Aerad House
PO BOX 10
Heathrow Airport
Middlesex
TW6 2JA

Civil Aviation Authority Printing & Publishing
Greville House
37 Gratton Road
Cheltenham
Glos.
GL50 2BN
Telephone 0242 35151

Jeppesen & Co. Gmb H
PO Box 160454
6000 Frankfurt/Main 16
Germany

Number 1 A.I.D.U.
RAF Northolt
West End Road
Ruislip
Middlesex
HA4 6NG

Avmail (Outdated aviation chart service)
9 Hitherwood
Cranleigh
Surrey.
GU6 8BN
SAE for catalogue.

In addition, many of the aviation hobby shops and Lowe Electronics, for example, carry stocks of outdated charts, maps and route supplements. Of course, prices vary greatly, but an average charge for an outdated airways chart is around £3.00.

APPENDIX 8. USEFUL ADDRESSES

Servisair Ltd.
Servisair House
PO BOX No. 22
Bramhall
Stockport
Cheshire
SK7 2DA
Telephone 061–440–0044

London Air Traffic Control Centre
Porters Way
West Drayton
Middlesex
UB7 9AX
Telephone 0895–445566

Scottish & Oceanic Air Traffic
Control Centre
Atlantic House
Sherwood Road
Prestwick
Ayrshire
KA9 2NR
Telephone 0292–79800

National Air Traffic Services
CAA House
45–49 Kingsway
London
WC2B 6TE
Telephone 071–379–7311

British Airways
Speedbird House
London Heathrow Airport
Hounslow
Midlesex
TW6 2JA
Telephone 081–759–5511

Ian Allan Ltd (publishers)
Coombelands House
Addlestone
Weybridge
Surrey
KT15 1HY
Telephone 0932–858511

Federal Aviation Authority
(ATT: Mr Warren Davis)
Air Traffic Publications Branch
 ATP-210
Room 411
800 Independence Avenue – South/
 West
Washington DC 20951
USA
Telephone 202–267–9224

The District Manager
Radiocommunications Agency
PO Box 2500
Nottingham

For any queries you may have
regarding what you may, or may not,
legally listen to via your airband radio
receivers.

Stansted Aviation Society
Peter Wright
271 Birchanger Lane
Birchanger
Bishop's Stortford
Herts CM23 5QP

Monthly members magazine *Stansted
Aviation Society News*.

The Aviation Society (TAS)
Mr Peter Hampson (Chairperson)
Spectator's Terraces
Manchester International Airport
Manchester M22 5SZ
Telephone 061–499–0303

Monthly members magazine *Winged
Words*.

LAAS International
M.W. Tatner
Mikalian
Blackmore Road
Kelvedon Hatch
Brentwood
Essex CM15 0AP

Monthly members magazine *Aviation
News & Review*.

Note. There are many more aviation societies around the country. Apart from
those listed here, I did not receive any other responses to my enquiries.

APPENDIX 9. AIRPORT, AIRCRAFT AND ICAO CODES

AIRLINE	2 CODE	3 CODE	AIRPORTS	CALLSIGN
ATI	BM	ATI	2	ATI
Adria Airways	JP	IAA	2,8,11,5,4	J/P
Aer Lingus	EI	EIN	1,2,8,9,10,7,5,3	Shamrock
Aeroflot	SU	AFL	1,2,4,5	Aeroflot
Aeromaritime	QK	QKL	2	Q/K
Aigle Azur	ZI	AAF	2,5	Z/I (Zulu-India)
Air 2000		AMM	2,4,9	Jetset
Air Algerie	AH	DAH	1	A/H
Air Atlantique	DG	AAG	2	Atlantic
Air Atlantis	TP	AIA	2,11,8,4	Atlantis
Air Bridge Carriers	AK	ABR	13,5,4,12	Air Bridge
Air Canada	AC	ACA	1,2,4,3	Air Canada
Air Ecosse	SM	ECS	4,5	Ecosse Air
Air Europa	UX	AEA	2,4,8,9,11,5,12	Air Europa
Air Europe	AE	AEL	2,4,8,9,12,5	Air Europe
Air France	AF	AFR	1,2,4,8,11,5	Air France
Air Furness	GB	AFW	4	G/B
Air Holland		AHD	2	Orange
Air India	AI	AIC	1	Air India
Air Lanka	UL	ALK	2	Air Lanka
Air Malta	KM	AMC	1,2,4,8,9,12,11,5	A/M/C
Air Malta (Charter)		KMC	2	K/M/C
Air Mauritius	MK	MAU	1	Air Mauritius
Air New Zealand	TE	ANZ	2	New Zealand
Air Seychelles	HM	SEY	2	Seychelles
Air UK	UK	UKA	1,2,10,11,5,4,3	UK
Air Vendee	VM	AVD	2	V/M
Air Yugoslavia		YRG	2,8,9	
Air Zimbabwe	UM	AZW	2	Zimbabwe
Alitalia	AZ	AZA	1,2	Alitalia
Altair		SM	12	
Amber Air		DMD	2	Amber
American Airlines	AA	AAL	2,4	American
American Trans Air		AMT	2,3	Amtran
Anglo Airlines	ML	ANC	2	Anglo
Arkia	IZ	AIZ	2	Arkia
Austrian Airlines	OS	AUA	1,2	Austrian
Austrian Charter	OB	AAT	2	Austrian Charter
Aviaco	AO	AYC	2,4,9,12,11,5	Aviaco
Aviogenex	JJ	AGX	2,4,8,11,5	J/J
BWIA International	BW	BWA	1	
Balair	BB	BBB	2,5	Balair
Balkan-Bulgarian Airlines	LZ	LAZ	1,2,4,8,12,11,5	L/Z
Baltic Airlines		HOT	2	
Bangladesh Biman	BG	BBC	1	Bangladesh
Birmingham Executive	VB	BEX	8	
Braathens SAFE	BU	BRA	2	Braathens

Brit Air	DB	BZH	2	D/B
Britannia Airways	BY	BAL	2,4,8,9,12,11,5,3	Britannia
British Air Ferries	VF	BAF	4,12,5	Air Ferry
British Airways	BA	BAW	1,2,4,8,11,5,3	Speedbird
British Island Airways	KD	BIA	2,12	Island
British Midland Airways	BD	BMA	1,8,9,10,7,12,5	Midland
British West Indian	BW	BWA	1	B/W
Brymon Airways	BC	BRY	1,2,8,6	Brymon
CAAC China	CA	CCA	2	China
CAS Czechoslovak	OK	CSA	1	CSA
CTA		CTA	2	CTA
Cal-Air International	EN	CAI	2,4,5,3	Caljet
Caledonian Airways	KT	BKT	2,4,8,9,11,3	Caledonian
Cameroon Airlines	UY	UYC	2	Camair
Canafrica		NCR	2,5	Nacar
Canadian Airlines Int.	CP	CPC	3	Empress
Capital Airlines	BZ	CPA	2,10,5	B/Z
Casair	TI	CSL	4	Casair
Cathay Pacific	CX	CPX	2	Cathay
Connectair	AX	CAX	2,4	A/X
Continental Airlines	CO	COA	2	Continental
Corse Air	SS	CSS	2	S/S
Cyprus Airways	CY	CYP	1,2,4,8,9,11,5	Cyprus
DLT	LH	DLH	2,4	Lufthansa
Dairo Air Services		DSR	2	Dairair
Dan-Air	DA	DAN	1,2,4,8,9,10,12,11,5,3	Danair
Delta Airlines	DL	DAL	2	Delta
Eagle Air	VL	ISL	2	Eagle
Egyptair	MS	MSR	1	Egyptair
El Al	LY	ELY	1,4	El Al
Emirates Airlines	EK	UAE	2	Emirates
Ethiopean Airlines	ET	ETH	1	Ethiopian
Euroair	EZ	URO	2	Euroair
Europe Air Services	EY	EYT	2	E/Y
Finnair	AY	FIN	1,4	Finnair
Flying Tigers	FT	FTL	5,1,3	Tiger
GB Airways	GT	GBL	2	Gibair
Gamair	QH	GAM	2	Gamair
Garuda	GA	GIA	2	Indonesia
Gas Air	GS	NGS	2	G/S
Ghana Airways	GH	GHA	1	Ghana
Gill Aviation		GIL	11	
Guernsey Airlines	GE	GER	2,4,11,5,3	Guernsey
Gulf Air	GF	GFA	1	Gulfair
Hispania Lineas	HI	HSL	2,4,8,9,11,5	H/I
Iberia	IB	IBE	1,4,5	Iberia
Icelandair	FI	ICE	1,5,3	Iceair
Inex Adria	JP	IAA	4,9,12,5	
Interflug	IF	IFL	2,4	Interflug
Iran Air	IR	IRA	1	Iranair
Iraqi Airways	IA	IAW	1	Iraqi
JAL Japan Airlines	JL	JAL	1	Japanair

JAT Yugoslav Airlines	JU	JAT	1,2,4,8,9,12,11,5	JAT
Jersey European Airways	JY	JEA	8,7	Jersey
KAR Air	KR	KAR	4,2	Kar Air
KLM Royal Dutch Airlines	KL	KLM	1,2,4,8,11,5,3	KLM
Kenya Airways	KQ	KQA	1	K/Q
Korean Air	KE	KAL	2	
Kuwait Airways	KU	KAC	1	K/U
LAC	CN	LIC	2	
LOT Polish Airlines	LO	LOT	1,4,5	LOT
Linjeflyg	LF	LIN	2	Swedline
Loganair	LC	LOG	4,5,3	Loganair
London City Airways	II	ECE	6	*Shared Service
Lufthansa	LH	DLH	1,2,8,5,4	Lufthansa
Luxair	LG	LGL	1	Luxair
Maersk Air	DM	DMA	2,5	Maerskair
Malaysian Airline System	MH	MAS	1	Malaysian
Malev Hungarian Airlines	MA	MAH	1	Malev
Malinair		MAK	5	Malin
Manx Airlines	JE	MNX	1,4,8,10,7,11,5	Manx
Martinair	MP	MPH	5	Martinair
Middle East Airlines	ME	MEA	1	Cedar Jet
Minerve	IW	MRV	2	
Monarch Airlines	OM	MON	2,4,8,9,12,5	Monarch
NFD	NS	NFD	4	Flamingo
NLM City Hopper	HN	NLM	1,2,8	City
Nationair Canada	NX	NXA	2	Nation Airways
Netherlines	WU	NET	8,9	Netherlines
Nigeria Airways	WT	NGA	1	Nigeria
Northwest Airlines	NW	NWA	2,3	Northwest
Norway Airlines		NOS	2	
Oasis		AAN	2,11,5	
Olympic Airways	OA	OAL	1	Olympic
PIA Pakistan	PK	PIA	1	Pakistan
Pan American	PA	PAA	1,3	Clipper Jet
Paramount		PAT	2,8,9,11,5	
Partnair		PAR	5	Partnair
Peregrine	PJ	PSS	9	
Philippine Airlines	PR	PAL	2	Philippine
Piedmont Airlines	PI	PAI	2	Piedmont
Qantas	QF	QFA	1,4	Qantas
RFG	VG	RFG	2	RFG
Royal Air Maroc	AT	RAM	1,2,4	Air Maroc
Royal Jordanian Airlines	RJ	RJA	1	Royal Jordanian
Ryanair	FR	RYR	2,4,8,5	
SAS	SK	SAS	1,2,4,5	Scandinavian
Sabena Belgian Airlines	SN	SAB	1,4,8	Sabena
Saudia Saudi Arabian	SV	SVA	1	Saudia
Scanair	DK	VKG	2	
Sierra Leone Airlines	LJ	SLA	2	Selair
Singapore Airlines	SQ	SIA	1,4	Singapore
South African Airways	SA	SAA	1	Springbok
Spanair	NR	SPP	2,9,11,5	Spanair

Spantax	BX	BXS	5,4	Spantax
Sterling	NB	SAW	2,5	Sterling
Suckling	CB	SAY	4	
Sudan Airways	SD	SUD	1	Sudanair
Sun D'or	ER	ERO	2	E/R
Swissair	SR	SWR	1,2,4,8,5	Swissair
TAP Air Portugal	TP	TAP	1,4,9,12,11,5	TAP
TAROM Romanian	RO	ROT	1,2,5,4	Tarom
TAT	IJ	TAT	2	I/J
TMA	TL	TMA	1	T/L
Thai International	TG	THA	1	Thai Inter
Toros Airlines		TAU	2,11	
Tradewinds Airways	IK	IKA	2,3	Tradewinds
Trans Arabian Air	TO	TRT	2	Trans Arabian
Trans Europa	TR	TEU	5	
Trans European	HE	TEA	2	H/E
Trans World Airways	TW	TWA	1,2,3	Trans World
Transavia	HV	TRA	2,5	Transavia
Tunis Air	TU	TAR	1,2,4,8,9,12,5	Tunisair
Turkish Airlines	TK	THY	1	
Uganda Airlines	QU	UGA	1	Q/U
Universair	UN	UNA	2,11,5,4	Universair
VARIG Brazilian Airlines	RG	VRG	1	Varig
VIASA Venezuelan Airlines	VA	VIA	1	Viasa
Virgin Atlantic	VS	VIR	2	Virgin
Viva Airlines		VIV	2	
Wardair Canada	WD	WDA	2,4,8,10,11,3	Wardair
World Airways	WO	WOA	2	World
Worldways Canada	WG	WWC	2,4,8,11,3	Worldways
Yemenia (Yemen)	IY	IYE	2	Yemeni
ZAS Egypt	WW	ZAS	2	Zas Airlines
Zambia Airways	QZ	ZAC	1	Zambia

Index

THE HF-225
GENERAL COVERAGE RECEIVER

Listen to the Long Haul air traffic

. You heard the Speedbird flight g handed over to Oceanic Con- n your VHF radio. But after that, t happens? Because VHF signals el in a straight line, the range is d to about 100 miles air to ground. that, all traffic is carried on HF ɔ using uencies w e e n lz and Hz. (In ɪ words short e bands.) der to lis- to Con- e calling New

will need something rather better. This is where our HF-225 comes in. Designed and produced in England, the HF-225 covers all frequencies between 30kHz and 30MHz. (In other words, from long wave broadcasting to the upper limit of short wave.) It will receive everything from Concorde to ships around the coast; from US aircraft over the gulf to R a d i o Baghdad (if you want to listen to Radio B a g h d a d) ;

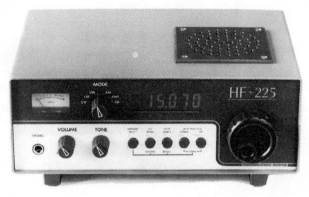

, you will need a short wave re- r that can listen in the single side- l (SSB) mode. This is one area e the average portable short wave ɔ will not give you results and you

from RAF Volmet to weather fax pictures (with a suitable decoder).
The HF-225. Your gateway to worldwide listening. Just one of the fine radios from Lowe Electronics.

*send four first class stamps to receive detailed information and a **FREE** ɔ of our "**Listener's Guide**"; the no-nonsense introduction to the great world of short wave listening.*

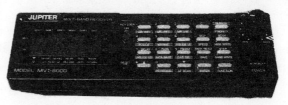

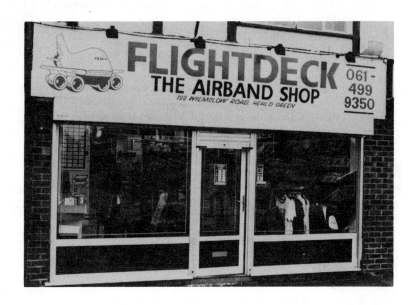